Collected Classics

Volume 5

Level 3

Pearson Education Limited
Edinburgh Gate, Harlow,
Essex CM20 2JE, England
and Associated Companies throughout the world.

ISBN 0 582 343593

This collection of classics first published 2000

Typeset by Refine Catch, Suffolk
Set in 11/14pt Bembo
Printed in Spain by Mateu Cromo, S. A. Pinto (Madrid)

Published by Pearson Education Limited in association with
Penguin Books Ltd, both companies being subsidiaries of Pearson Plc

Contents

The Man with Two Shadows and Other Ghost Stories

MARK LEMON, JOSEPH SHERIDAN LE FANU,
TOM HOOD and CATHERINE CROWE

Level 3

Retold by Louise Greenwood
Series Editors: Andy Hopkins and Jocelyn Potter

Contents

Introduction

I knew it was there before I turned and saw it at the top of the stairs. Everyone went silent. Then one of the men picked up his gun and shot at it, but nothing happened. The thing just smiled...

Do you want to know about ghosts? There are many kinds. There are ghosts who tell people about death and danger, like the old man of the Bank of England, and the thin, white man of Varley Grange. There are ghosts who come back to find their murderer, like the sailor who died at sea. There are ghosts of people who can never rest because of the things they did, like that of Jacopo Ferraldi. There are ghosts of living men too – men in prison for crimes that they did not do. And men who see terrible things, and ghosts before they die ...

In these six stories you will meet all these, and more. Now, do you *really* want to know about ghosts?

Ghost stories were much more popular in the 1800s than in the 1700s. In the 1700s there were no secrets in life. People believed that science could explain everything. They were not interested in dreams or ghosts or things that they could not understand.

Then, at the beginning of the 1800s, people became bored with amusing and clever stories about real life. They wanted stories about things that science and reason could not explain. Stories about strange, foreign countries, about ghosts in big, dark houses and about mysterious animals in shadowy forests. Stories about brave young men who saved beautiful young women from death and terrible danger. People wanted stories to frighten them.

These stories were called 'Gothic' stories. Three of the most popular early Gothic stories were John Polidori's *The Vampyre* (1818), Mary Shelley's *Frankenstein* (1819), and Sir Walter Scott's *Three Tales of Terror* (1824–1828).

5

Then, in the middle of the 1800s, the ghost story changed. Ghosts moved out of large, dark houses in foreign lands, and moved into ordinary houses in everyday life. Ghosts walked along streets and around gardens, and came through windows into ordinary homes. Nobody was safe. It was easier to believe in ghosts and they became even more frightening.

Charles Dickens (1812–1870) wrote many ghost stories. Two of his most famous are *A Christmas Carol* (1852) and *The Signalman* (1866). He liked ghost stories so much that he started a magazine for them in 1859. Many famous writers wrote for this magazine, including Wilkie Collins, Elizabeth Gaskell, Mark Lemon and Joseph Sheridan Le Fanu. Le Fanu's stories were unusual because his ghosts were often not just in the same room, but inside the person's head.

Towards the end of the 1800s, ghost story writers followed Le Fanu's example more and more. They became interested in questions like: When does a man stop being a man? When does he start to become something different? This was the most frightening kind of story of all. It was impossible to escape from the ghost, because it lived inside you. It drank your blood and ate your heart and mind and you went crazy.

The most famous books of this type were Robert Louis Stevenson's *Dr Jekyll and Mr Hyde* (1886), Oscar Wilde's *The Picture of Dorian Gray* (1891), and Bram Stoker's *Dracula* (1897).

All the stories in this book were written in the middle of the 1800s, at the time when ghost stories took place in everyday life.

Joseph Sheridan Le Fanu (1814–73) was born in Dublin, Ireland, and studied at Trinity College, Dublin. He worked for newspapers for many years. After his wife died he stayed at home and saw few people. He wrote over 20 books, but he is best known for his clever ghost stories. His books *House by the Churchyard* (1863), *Uncle Silas* (1864) and his book of short stories *In a Glass Darkly* (1872) include some of the most frightening stories in the English language.

Mark Lemon (1809–70) was a businessman before he became a writer. He wrote songs, Christmas stories and joke books, but most of his writing was for the theatre. In 1851 he wrote a short, funny play with Charles Dickens called *Mr Nightingale's Diary*, and they acted in it together. He is most famous for starting the British magazine *Punch*.

Tom Hood (1835–74) was the son of the famous writer, Thomas Hood. Like his father, he wrote poems, but he is mostly famous for his amusing writing. He wrote for newspapers and wrote many children's books, often working with his sister. He also drew the pictures for many of his books.

Catherine Crowe (1800–76) was born in the south of England but lived in Edinburgh, Scotland, for many years. Her real name was Catherine Stevens. She wrote a lot of children's books and other stories, but her most popular book was a book of ghost stories, *The Night Side of Nature* (1848).

The Dead Man of Varley Grange

Anonymous, 1878

'Hallo, Jack. Where are you going? Are you staying with your parents for Christmas?' Jack Darent and I were in the army together. It was December the 23rd and everyone was going away for the holiday.

Jack stood in the doorway, tall and good-looking, laughing at my question. 'Not this year. I've had enough of old aunts and my sister's six children. I'm not a family man like you. By the way, how is your beautiful sister?'

'She's very well and going to lots of parties,' I answered, smiling.

Jack looked a little sad at this. He was in love with my sister and she was in love with him, but they did not have enough money to get married. 'Well, please send her my love,' he said. 'I'm going down to your part of England – Westernshire – for some shooting. Henderson has asked me and some others. We're staying in an old house, where I hear the shooting is very good. Perhaps you know it? It's called Varley Grange.'

'Varley Grange?' I said. 'Oh no, Jack. You can't go there.'

'Why not?' he asked, surprised.

'I've heard ... uncomfortable things about that house,' I said, searching for the right words.

'Uncomfortable? What do you mean?' laughed Jack. 'It'll probably be a bit cold and there'll be a few rats maybe, but Henderson's French cook is coming and he's bringing lots of wine. I'm sure I won't feel the cold.'

'No, Jack. I don't think you quite understand ...' I began. I think he thought I was a bit crazy.

'Well, I must go, or I'll miss the train. See you after Christmas,' he said happily, not hearing my last words, and he was gone.

When I got home, my wife, my sister Bella, and my two children were all waiting for me to have tea.

'I've just seen Jack Darent, Bella,' I said.

'Oh yes,' she answered, pretending not to be interested. 'And where's he going for Christmas?'

'You'll be surprised when I tell you. He's going to Varley Grange.'

'Varley Grange?' she said. 'But that's terrible! Did you try to stop him?'

'Of course I did, but he didn't understand.'

She did not wait to hear any more, but ran out of the room, crying.

My wife was very confused. She was from London, not Westernshire, and she did not know the story of Varley Grange. 'Why is she crying?' she asked. 'What is this place you're talking about?'

'Well, my dear, do you believe in ghosts?' I asked her.

'Of course not,' she said, looking at the children, who were listening carefully. 'Wait, let me take the children out.'

When the children were playing happily in another room, I told her the story. 'Varley Grange is an old house in Westernshire. It belonged to the Varley family – all of them are dead now. The last two members of the family, Dennis Varley and his sister, lived there a hundred years ago. The sister fell in love with a poor man and her brother didn't want them to marry. To stop them, he locked her up. One night she and her lover ran away, but her brother caught her and took her back to Varley Grange, where he killed her.'

'He murdered his own sister?'

'Yes. And since that day, Dennis Varley's ghost has walked around the house. Many people have seen it. They say that if you

Bella did not wait to hear any more, but ran out of the room, crying.

also see the ghost of his sister, you will have very bad luck or a serious illness, or perhaps you'll even die.'

Of course, my wife did not believe the story and we all forgot about it until a week later when I saw Jack again, sitting in a London café.

'Well, Jack, how was the shooting?' I asked. From his white face I saw that all was not well. He asked me to sit down.

'I understand now what you were saying before I left London,' he began. 'I'm only sorry I didn't listen to you.'

'Did you see something?' I asked.

'I saw everything,' he whispered. 'Let me tell you what happened. We all left London together and had a good journey down to Westernshire. We were all very happy and that night we slept well. The next day, we went shooting. It was wonderful – birds everywhere. We shot about two hundred altogether, and

Henderson's French cook made us a wonderful dinner from them. After the food we all sat around drinking coffee, smoking and telling stories about shooting and fishing. Suddenly one of us – I can't remember who it was – shouted and pointed up to the top of the stairs. We all looked round and there was a man looking down at us.'

'How was he dressed?' I asked.

'He was wearing black clothes, but it was his face that I noticed most. It was white and thin and he had a long beard and terrible eyes. He looked like a dead man. As we watched he went into my bedroom and everyone ran to the stairs. We searched all the rooms but could find nothing.

'Well, none of us slept very well that night, but the next morning at breakfast, Henderson asked us not to talk about it any more. He seemed quite angry and did not want the servants to hear. We had another good day's shooting and we all slept well that night. Two nights went by and nothing happened. Then, on the third night, we were sitting by the fire after dinner as before, when suddenly the room went cold. I knew it was there before I turned and saw it at the top of the stairs. Everyone went silent. Then one of the men picked up his gun and shot at it, but nothing happened. The thing just smiled and, once again, went into my bedroom.

'The next morning, four out of the eight of us decided to leave immediately. Some said they had important business in London, others suddenly remembered that they had to see their families. Anyway, there were four of us left – Wells, Harford, Henderson and myself. In the morning, we were all happy and laughing about the ghost and we decided that someone from the village was probably making fools of us. Henderson told us the story he heard from one of the villagers about Dennis Varley's murder of his sister. I'm sure you know it, so I won't tell you again.'

'We saw the dead man coming slowly up the stairs.'

'Yes, I do know it,' I said. 'I also know that anyone who sees the ghosts of both Dennis and his sister will have terrible bad luck.'

'Not only that,' said Jack. 'Anyone who sees the sister's face will die within one year.' His face turned whiter as he said this and he did not speak for a few minutes. Then he continued his story.

'Well, that night we felt far less brave than in the morning. At eleven o'clock we all waited in different places for the ghosts to come. I was at the top of the stairs with Harford opposite me. There was a storm outside and the wind made a sound like someone crying. At midnight there was a scream from Henderson downstairs and Harford and I jumped up. We saw the dead man coming slowly up the stairs towards us. Henderson ran after it and, as the ghost passed us, we felt cold and terribly afraid.

13

Then, suddenly, Harford held my arm and pointed. I turned and saw the ghost of the sister coming. She wore a long, black and white dress and she had a big cross round her neck. I could not see her face, but I wanted to – I don't know why, I couldn't stop myself. I went towards her and, as I did so, she looked up.'

'You saw her face? What was it like?' I asked.

'I saw it,' he said, 'but I can never describe it to anyone.'

'Well, what happened next?' I asked.

'I can't remember. I think I fell. Everything just went black. I left the house the next day. I know that I'll die in a year and something terrible will happen to Harford. He saw her too, but not her face. The others only saw the brother.'

I decided not to tell my sister the terrible story, but soon things happened which everyone heard about. Bob Harford's wife ran away from him two days after they got married. He has gone to live in a wild part of Canada and no one hears from him any more. And Jack Darent? Poor, handsome Jack Darent died in South Africa about eleven months after I met him in the café that day. And my sister Bella? She is still beautiful, but she always wears black and she always looks sad.

The Ghost Detective

Mark Lemon, 1866

When I first came to London thirty years ago, I met a young man, James Loxley, who worked in the wine business. The company he worked for sold wine to pubs and restaurants, and just after I met him he got a new job in the company with more money. Because of this he was able to get married and I went to his wedding. His wife was a pretty girl with fair hair and blue eyes. It was clear to everyone that they loved each other.

14

They went to live in a new house outside London and I visited them often. Over the next three years, they had two beautiful children and they were a very happy family. They did not have much money and had only one servant, a rather stupid girl called Susan. One year they asked me to come to their home for Christmas dinner. We had a lovely meal and then sat in their sitting-room, laughing and talking. It was a small but comfortable room. In the corner was a Christmas tree and on the wall was a painting of Loxley's mother and father, who were both dead. Loxley loved this painting. He told me that it was just like his parents and he often felt that they were really in the room with him.

After Christmas Loxley came with me to visit my old uncle for a few days. He seemed very quiet during the trip and I thought perhaps he wanted to be with his wife and children. When the holiday was over, we travelled to London together early in the morning to go to work. He seemed worried during the journey but he did not say why. The next day I could not believe it when I heard that he was in prison for stealing money from his company. I immediately went to see him and on the way I remembered his quietness over the last few days. I also began to think about how expensive it was with two children and how Loxley probably needed money. But, no, it was impossible. I knew that he was an honest man.

At the prison I talked to him and this is the story he told me:

'On December the 24th, Christmas Eve, I went to one of my customers, John Rogers, and asked him to pay his bill. He is often late with payments and I wanted to get the money before the Christmas holiday. He gave me a cheque and I immediately took it to the bank and cashed it, because in the past this customer has written a cheque and then stopped it before we could get the cash. It was too late to go to the office, so I decided to keep the money until after the holiday. I put it in my pocket and went

Loxley told me that it was just like his parents and he often felt that they were really in the room with him.

home. On the day we left my house to visit your uncle, I could not find the money and I became very worried. I looked all over the house, but it was nowhere. I was afraid to go back to work. When I told my boss about it, he did not understand why I didn't come to the office immediately when I couldn't find the money. He did not believe my story and called me a thief.'

At that moment we heard someone crying and screaming outside the door. It was Loxley's wife, Martha. She ran in, held her husband in her arms and cried and cried. It was terrible to see. After some time the prison guard told us to leave, and I took her home, still crying. She became ill and her mother came to stay with her and the children. The servant, Susan, was also there. She seemed to be a good girl and was always ready to help, but she seemed very unhappy about the problem and sometimes cried more than Martha. I visited the little house almost every day and, one day, I found Martha very excited.

'What's happened, Martha?' I asked.

'Well, you probably won't believe this,' she said, 'but last night I saw my husband's ghost.'

'But James isn't dead,' I said, 'he's only in prison.'

'I know, I know,' she said, 'but listen to this. Last night at midnight I was in the sitting-room – I couldn't sleep as usual. I was sitting worrying about our problems. Suddenly I looked up and saw James come into the room without a sound. He sat down over there in his favourite chair and looked at the picture of his father for a few minutes without speaking. Then he stood up and looked at me with a face full of love and walked out of the room.'

'Perhaps you were half asleep and dreamed it,' I said, but she was sure about what happened and did not want to listen to me.

Susan, the servant girl, was in the room with us and was listening to the conversation, looking very afraid. 'Did you speak to the ghost, Mrs Loxley? Did it say anything to you?' she asked.

'No, Susan. I've told you everything that happened,' said Martha.

I left the house that day feeling very worried as Martha was looking so white and tired. I thought about calling a doctor, but I decided to wait and see what happened. The next day I visited them again and found Martha even more excited.

'He came again,' she almost shouted. 'This time he stood in front of the painting of his father and pointed at it. Then he turned to me and held out his arms. I ran towards him, but he disappeared and I crashed into the wall. I think he means there is something behind the picture. Please, will you help me to take it down and look?'

The painting was quite high on the wall and I needed a ladder to reach it. I called Susan and asked her to bring one.

'This time James stood in front of the painting of his father and pointed at it.'

'A ladder?' she asked. 'What for?'

When I explained about the painting I was surprised to see her face turn white. 'There isn't a ladder,' she said quickly.

'But I'm sure I saw one,' I said, 'just outside the kitchen door. Oh well, my mistake. Don't worry.'

Susan didn't leave the room but watched as I stood on a chair and began to take the picture of Loxley's father down. Suddenly she screamed, 'It was me, Mrs Loxley. I know why the ghost came. The money's behind the picture. I hid it there.' She began to cry and cry, and it was some time before she could tell the story.

'It was on Christmas Eve,' she said. 'Mr Loxley came home a bit late. I was behind him as he was walking upstairs, and he took his handkerchief out of his pocket. As he did so, the money fell out. He didn't notice, but I did and I picked it up. It was more money than I've seen in my life, Mrs Loxley, I couldn't stop myself. Then I was frightened about someone finding it on me or in my room, so I hid it behind that picture. Oh, please Mrs Loxley. Don't send me to prison.'

Well, as soon as Susan told her story to the police, James was a free man, and the family are now living happily in Australia.

The Dream

Joseph Sheridan Le Fanu, 1838

In the year 1750 I was working at the church in Castleton, a small town in the south of England. One night a knock at the door woke me up. Outside was a poor little girl, crying loudly. After a few minutes, I understood that her father was very ill, almost dying, and she wanted me to come to him.

'Of course I'll come,' I said. 'Where do you live? Who is your father?' She did not answer but began to cry more loudly. Again I waited until she was calm, and then asked her the same question.

'My father is Pat Connell,' she said, 'and now I'm sure that you won't come.

I knew about Pat Connell. He was a bad man, who often stole things, and he drank too much beer. I never saw him in church. He was a bad man, but he was dying and I had to go to him, to say a few words to help him as he died.

I put on my coat and followed the poor little girl through the cold, dark streets. We walked quickly and our way took us to the worst part of the town. The streets were narrow, the houses were old and there was a terrible smell. The girl went through a small door and I followed her up the broken stairs to the top of the building. She took me up to the bedroom where her father lay. His wife and children were sitting round the bed watching worriedly. The doctor was also with him. I went closer to the man and looked at his face, which was blue from too much drink. His lips were black and, from his breathing, I felt sure that death was not far away.

'Is there any hope?' I asked the doctor. He shook his head and listened to the man's heart.

'This man is dead,' he said, and turned away from the bed.

The wife and children began to cry. I stood still, watching them, feeling sad that I was too late to help the dead man, too late to talk to him about God.

Suddenly the wife screamed and pointed at the bed. I turned round quickly and saw the body of the man sitting up in bed. For a few seconds I could not move. I stood, confused, thinking of dead men and ghosts until I realized that the man was alive. The doctor ran to look at him and found blood running from a cut in the man's body.

'The blood coming out has made him better,' he said. 'I've never seen this before. He's very lucky.'

The doctor and the man's wife made him comfortable, and I

I turned round quickly and saw the body of the man sitting up in bed.

left, promising to return the next day. I did go back the next day and the day after, but the sick man was always sleeping. On the third day I returned and found him awake. As I went in, he shouted, 'Oh, thank you, thank you for coming. I want to talk to you.' I sat down next to the bed and he began to talk.

'I've been a very bad man, I know that,' he said. 'I've stolen, I've drunk too much, I've had a bad life, but I don't want to go to hell.' He began to cry and could not stop for some time. I gave him a glass of water and he continued. 'I must tell you what happened that night you came here. I know you'll understand as a man of the church. I came in late after drinking a lot of beer. I went to bed but woke up a few hours later. I wanted to get some air but I didn't want to wake the children by opening the window, so I started to go downstairs. As it was very dark I counted the stairs so that I did not fall at the bottom. Well, I got to the bottom of the first stairs, but suddenly the floor broke under me and I started to fall.

'I fell and fell for a long time through the blackness and when I stopped I was at a big table. Sitting at the table were lots of men. There was a smell of fire all around and the light was red. Suddenly, I realized that I was in hell. I was dead. I opened my mouth to scream, but no sound came out. I tried to stand up. I wanted to run away, but the man sitting next to me put his hand on my shoulder. "Sit down, my friend. You can *never* leave this place," he said. His voice was weak, like a child's. Then at the end of the table the tallest of the men stood up. I felt that he was able to control me; he seemed very strong, and he had such a terrible face. He pointed at me with his long, black finger. "You can leave now," he said in a frightening voice, "but you must promise to come back in three months' time." I shouted, "I promise to come back, but in God's name let me go now." The next thing I knew I was sitting up in bed and the doctor was there. Oh, please tell me, was it hell? Did I go to hell or was it just a terrible dream? I don't want to go back.'

I thought carefully, and then I said, 'Pat, I'm sure it was a dream, which you felt strongly because you were ill, but it is also a warning to you. Only bad people go to hell. If you live a good life from now, if you stop drinking and stealing and come to church, you will not go back down there.'

When I left he was looking much happier. A few days later, I visited the house again and found him much better. He was mending the floor at the bottom of the first stairs. 'This was where I went through. I just want to be safe,' he explained.

For several weeks Pat Connell was a different man. He stopped drinking and stealing, he worked hard to look after his family, and he came to church every Sunday. One day I met him in the street, coming home from work. We spoke a few words and when I left him he looked happy and well. But a few days later, he was dead.

'When I woke up, I saw two people going silently out of the room.'

I went to see his wife and she told me what happened. 'Pat was doing so well. I was proud of the way he stopped drinking, but one night he met an old friend, just returned from the army. He was so pleased to see him that, without thinking, he went into the pub with this friend. Well, of course, they started drinking, and one beer followed another. His friends had to carry him home and we all put him in his bed. I stayed down here by the fire. I was feeling sad, thinking about all our problems. I think I fell asleep for a few minutes. When I woke up, I saw two people, one of them my husband, Pat, going silently out of the room. I called to him, "Pat, where are you going?" but he didn't answer me. The door closed. Then I heard a terrible crash from above. I ran up the first stairs and there was Pat. He was dead – his back was broken. I think he was coming down from the bedroom when he fell at the bottom of the first stairs, you know, the place he was mending when you came to visit.'

I remembered the place well. The place which, in Pat's dream, was the entrance to hell. The place where he knew he had to go back.

The Man with Two Shadows

(from The Shadow of a Shade, Tom Hood, 1869)

My sister Lettie had lived with me ever since I got married. She is my wife's best friend and my children all love her, but her face is always sad. Many men have asked her to marry them but she has always said no, since she lost her first real love.

George Mason was my wife's cousin, a sailor. He and Lettie met at our wedding and fell in love immediately. George was a brave man, who loved the sea, and I was not surprised when he decided to travel to the Arctic on a ship called the *Pioneer*. Lettie was afraid when he told her, but she could not stop him. I knew that she was worried because, for the first time in her life, she began to look sad sometimes.

My younger brother Harry liked painting, so he decided to paint a picture of George before he left. It was quite a good picture. I thought the face was too white but Lettie was very pleased with it and she put it on the wall in our sitting-room.

Before the ship sailed, George met the ship's doctor, a Scotsman called Vincent Grieve. He brought him to dinner with us and I disliked him immediately. He was a tall, thin man with fair hair and cold, grey eyes. His face looked hard and I felt sure that he was not honest. He sat too close to Lettie and seemed more like her lover than George. At first George did not notice, but Lettie did and she was unhappy about it. The strangest thing was when he saw the picture of George on the wall. He sat down opposite it, but stood up as soon as he saw it. 'I'm sorry,' he said, 'but I cannot look at that picture.'

'Well, I know it's not very good . . .' I began.

'It's not that it's either good or bad. I know nothing about painting,' he said. 'It's the eyes . . . they seem to follow me everywhere.'

I thought that perhaps he just wanted to move closer to Lettie, but when I saw his face, he looked really quite frightened.

At the end of the evening I quietly asked George about Vincent Grieve. 'Do you want to bring him to dinner again?' I whispered.

'No,' he answered. 'He's a good friend on the ship, but I don't like the way he is with ladies.'

We were all surprised when Vincent came again the next day. He brought a note for Lettie from George and after that he came almost every day. George was busier than him and did not have so much time to see Lettie. On the last day before the ship sailed, Vincent said to Lettie, 'If anything happens to George, I will still love you and you can marry me.'

Vincent Grieves said, 'It's the eyes . . . they seem to follow me everywhere.'

Lettie was very angry and told him to leave the house at once. She did not tell George about it because she wanted him to leave happily. The time came for George and Lettie to say goodbye and, when he left, Lettie cried for hours. I went in and put my arm around her. As I looked up, I noticed the picture of George on the wall. The face looked very, very white and I thought there was water on it. Perhaps it's just the light, I thought to myself and tried to forget about it.

The *Pioneer* sailed. George sent two letters, and then a year passed before we heard anything. We once read about the ship in the newspaper, but that was all. Spring-time came, and one beautiful warm evening we were all at home. The children were playing outside and Harry was watching them from the window. Suddenly the room felt very cold. Lettie looked up. 'How strange,' she said. 'Do you feel how cold it is?'

'Just like the weather in the Arctic,' I said. As I spoke, I looked at the picture on the wall and what I saw made me terribly afraid. His face suddenly looked like a dead man's, with no eyes. Without thinking, I said 'Poor George.'

'What do you mean?' asked Lettie, looking frightened. 'Have you heard something about George?'

'No, no,' I said quickly. 'I was just thinking about the cold weather where he is.'

At this moment, Harry put his head back into the room. 'Cold?' he said. 'Who's cold?'

'Did you not feel cold just then?' asked Lettie. 'We both did.'

'Not at all,' he said happily. 'How can you feel cold on a beautiful spring evening like this?'

I followed him out of the room. 'Harry,' I said, 'what's the date today?'

'It's Tuesday, February the 23rd. Look, here's the newspaper.'

I told him about the change in the picture and the cold feeling and asked him to write it down. I was sure that George was in some kind of trouble and I wanted to remember everything about that evening.

Later Lettie went to bed with a terrible cold and was ill all through the night. My wife was angry with me for sitting with the windows open and making my sister ill.

Early the next morning there was a knock at the door. It was Harry, looking white and frightened. I knew immediately why he was there.

'Have you seen the newspaper?' he asked.

On the front page was the news that George was dead. One sentence from the newspaper stayed in my mind: 'Lieutenant George Mason was out shooting with the ship's doctor, Vincent Grieve, when he died.'

When I told my wife about George, she began to cry. 'How can we tell poor Lettie?' she said.

'Ssssshh,' said Harry, but it was too late. Lettie was at the door and we had to tell her everything. She fell to the floor, her face as white as paper. We called the doctor immediately, but she was ill for many months.

About two months later, I read about the arrival of the *Pioneer*, George's ship, in Britain. I did not tell Lettie about it as she was only just getting better. A day or two after this there was a knock at the door and, as I got up to open it, I noticed George's picture once again. This time, to my surprise, he held one finger up and seemed to be warning me. I looked harder at George's face and was almost sure that I could see blood on it. I walked closer and saw that the warning finger was really a small moth, sitting on the picture. I picked up the sleepy moth and put

I walked closer and saw that the warning finger was really a small moth.

it under a wineglass. As I did this, the servant came in and said, 'Dr Vincent Grieve is here to see you, sir.'

As the doctor came in, I saw his face turn white. 'Please, cover that picture of George,' he said. 'It is even harder for me to look at it now that he is dead.'

I covered the picture and Grieve sat down. He looked very thin and white and, again, I felt a strong dislike for him. I asked him about the day George died and he told me the story.

'We were out shooting on the ice,' he said. 'It was not easy to walk. Suddenly, George fell. I tried to catch him . . . I threw my coat for him . . . I wanted to pull him up, but it was impossible. He fell into the ice-cold sea and slowly his head went under. His last words were "Say goodbye to her".'

As he finished his story, Grieve looked up. He screamed loudly and jumped up, pointing behind me. I looked round. The picture was uncovered again and George's white face looked down on us. I covered it again and Grieve seemed to feel better.

'I'm so sorry,' he said, 'I've been ill.' He stood up. 'I'm sorry,' he said again. Then he noticed the little white moth, which was still under the wineglass. 'Has someone else from the *Pioneer* been here?' he asked.

'No,' I answered. 'You are the first.'

'Then how did this moth get here? It only lives in the Arctic. That's very strange . . . Well, look after it. It's very unusual.'

He left a few minutes later and Harry and I watched him walk down the street. 'There's something I don't like about that man,' I said.

'You're right,' Harry said. 'Do you know he has two shadows? There's someone or something always standing at his side. That explains why he's always so frightened.'

We decided not to tell Lettie about his visit.

Two days later, I arrived home and found my sister very angry. 'Grieve came here today and asked me to marry him. He said that George wanted it. I couldn't believe it. We were in the sitting-room and he was standing by the wall. As he was speaking, there was a sound of something breaking, and George's picture fell on his head and cut it open. We had to carry him upstairs and call the doctor.'

I went angrily upstairs but, when I saw Grieve, it was clear that he could understand nothing. We could not move him and a nurse came to stay with him during the night. At about midnight, the nurse felt something was wrong in the room. She saw his two shadows on the wall and, frightened, went to get Lettie to sit with her. As soon as my sister came into the room, Grieve sat up and started to talk. 'I could not stop myself,' he said. 'I hit you with my gun because I loved her and now she'll never forgive me. I murdered you, George, because I loved her. Don't you see? Can't you understand? Please, please leave me alone.' As he shouted the last words, he got out of bed and walked backwards slowly, all the time looking at something following him, his eyes wide and afraid. He came to the window and suddenly seemed to decide something. Very quickly, he turned round, and Lettie could not stop him. Two days later, the police found his body in the river.

Now the picture of George is always covered. It has not changed again. Only Lettie's face has changed – she never laughs or smiles now.

The Ghost in the Bank of England

Anonymous, 1879

1

Many stories end with a wedding. Mine begins with one. The day that I married Annie Burdon was one of the happiest of my life. Everyone said we were crazy. We had no money and I was a young doctor with no job, but we loved each other.

After the wedding we were very poor and I could not find a job. I tried everywhere until, one day, I found a job as a doctor on a ship, sailing to Jamaica. I did not want to leave Annie, but I was not able to choose – I had to get some money.

The name of the ship was the *Darien* and my boss was Mr Julius Mendez, a small man of about fifty years old. Nobody liked him and, after one day at sea, I began to feel the same. He thought about one thing only – his health. He came to see me two or three times a day, worried about his heart, his stomach, his head or some other part of his body.

When we arrived at Kingston in Jamaica, Mr Mendez came to see me and said, 'I'm not sure if you will believe this, but I am in danger of dying before the end of my fifty-seventh year. I will be fifty-eight on September the 10th, and after midnight on that day I will be safe and able to live a long life. I cannot explain why or how I know this, but believe me it is true. I am frightened of dying and I don't like the doctors here. Please will you stay with me as my doctor and look after me? I will pay you well and after midnight on September the 10th you will be free to leave.'

At the end of the first month he paid me £50, which I immediately sent to Annie. The second month seemed very long. I was with Mr Mendez all day and all night because he was so worried, but he was healthy all the time. At last September the 10th came and Mr Mendez did not die. He thanked me and gave me my money, which I sent to Annie. My plan was to leave Jamaica on the *Darien*, but I became ill and it was a long time before I could start my journey home.

2

I looked like a ghost when I arrived home many months later. Annie was living with her brother and all the family thought I was dead. I was so happy when I saw my family again, but soon I started to worry. I still had no job and I was weak after my illness in Jamaica. I looked for a job in an office — anything for money — but it was still impossible. I found nothing.

One day I was looking for a pen on Annie's desk, when I noticed a letter from Jamaica.

'Oh, yes. I forgot all about that letter,' said Annie, 'it arrived while you were away.'

I opened it and found a letter from Julius Mendez. The letter said.

September the 12th, 1832

Dear Wilson,
You probably thought it was strange that I did not really thank you for your work. I am sending you this cheque, which I hope will help you.

Yours faithfully,
Julius Mendez

With the letter was a cheque for £1,000! At first I thought I was dreaming. All these months we were poor and worried about money and the cheque was sitting on Annie's desk. We were so happy. I immediately wrote a letter of thanks to Mr Mendez and then decided to go to London the next day to

With the letter was a cheque for £1,000!

cash the cheque. I had to take it to the Bank of England.

On the journey I met Mr Deacon, one of our neighbours.

'Where are you going, young Wilson?' he asked.

'I have to go to the Bank of England,' I answered.

'Ah,' he said, smiling, 'do you know I worked there as a cashier for twenty years. I still remember my desk . . . it was a lucky one. I haven't been back there for forty years.'

'A lucky desk?' I asked, surprised.

'Oh, yes,' he said, 'everyone in the bank knew that some desks were lucky and some were unlucky. Men who sat in some desks did very well and got better jobs, others . . . well . . . I can tell you about one unlucky desk as an example. A young man called Fred Hawes sat there. He was a good-looking, happy young man and he had a beautiful sister, Nancy who loved her brother very much. She worked hard to make more money for the family and she always looked after Fred. All the cashiers were in love with her and many young men, including myself, asked her to marry them, but she always said no. There was one young man, Isaac Ayscough, who was a close friend of Fred's. Nancy was frightened of him. She knew Isaac loved her but she only felt afraid of him and was always worried about Fred spending time with him. One day there was a problem at the bank. Some money disappeared and Isaac said that Fred was the thief. Fred went to prison and died there. Of course, his sister was very unhappy and became a little – well, odd. She came to the bank every day after Fred died and she always asked the same question, "Is my brother, Mr Frederick, here today?" and one of us always answered, "No, miss, not today." Then she always said, "Give my love to him when he returns and say I'll call tomorrow." One day she didn't come and we heard that she was dead.'

'And what about Isaac Ayscough?' I asked.

'Well,' continued Mr Deacon, 'after Fred's death, they moved him from a lucky desk to Fred's old, unlucky one. He came to work every day at the same time and left at the same time. He never spoke to anyone. He never married, but lived alone in a small room. He died suddenly at the age of fifty. Now they say that his ghost always comes to the bank when someone cashes the cheque of a dead man. Many people have seen it.'

As Mr Deacon finished his story, our journey ended and we said goodbye.

3

Soon I was walking in the busy streets of London. When I came to the Bank of England, I took the cheque from my pocket and looked at it again. I wanted to be sure it was real. I went into the bank and at first I felt confused. There were so many desks with

*I went into the bank and at first I felt confused. There were so many
desks with cashiers behind them.*

cashiers behind them – I did not know which one to go to. Then I noticed one of the cashiers looking at me. He was older than the other cashiers and was standing behind them. His clothes looked odd, perhaps from some years ago, and his face looked strange – thin and white, like a dead man's. He had a red scar on his face in the shape of a letter Y. The other cashiers were busy, so I gave him my cheque. I took the £1,000 banknote from him and left the bank quickly, feeling uneasy. But I returned home a rich man.

4

Everything was wonderful for a year. I found a job and we lived well. I enjoyed my work as a doctor. Then one day I was surprised to find a man from the Bank of England and a policeman at my house. They asked lots of questions about my cheque and the £1,000 banknote. I answered them all and they left, but the next day they returned. They said that my £1,000 banknote was not real, and that night I found myself in prison. I could not believe it. How could the note not be real? The police asked me the same questions again, and again I gave the same answers. They asked me about the cheque from Mr Mendez.

'What was the date on the cheque, Mr Wilson?' asked the detective.

'It was the same date as the letter, September the 12th,' I answered. 'Look, here it is.'

'I think *you* wrote the letter and the cheque, Mr Wilson. Do you know why? We have heard from the police in Jamaica that Mr Mendez died on September the 11th. Now how do you think he wrote a letter and a cheque to you on the 12th? He was already dead. You say that you cashed the cheque at the Bank of England. The banknote is not a real one – how do you explain that? The number on it is not from the Bank of England. Perhaps you made it yourself?'

I was so confused I could not speak. How did Mr Mendez die on September the 11th? That was the day after I left him and the day before he wrote my cheque. It was impossible. All I knew was that I was not crazy and I was not a criminal. 'Take me to the Bank of England,' I said, 'and I will show you the cashier who took my cheque and gave me the £1,000 banknote.'

5

Mr Deacon, the man who travelled with me to London that day and told me the ghost story, heard about my troubles. He liked me and felt sorry for me, so he came to visit me in prison. 'I'll come with you and the detective to the bank, tomorrow,' he said. 'Perhaps I'll be able to help.'

We arrived at the bank early the next day. The detective told me to look carefully at all the cashiers. Of course, I could not see the strange older man in his odd clothes anywhere.

'He's not here,' I said quietly.

'I knew it – a waste of time,' said the detective angrily. 'Of course he's not here.'

Mr Deacon stopped him. 'Wait,' he said, 'can you describe the cashier?'

I told them about the man's strange, old clothes, his thin, white face and the red scar in the shape of a letter Y. 'He didn't look alive,' I said, 'he looked more like a dead man.'

'That's because he *was* dead,' said Mr Deacon. 'You saw the ghost of Isaac Ayscough. Do you remember the story I told you that day? Do you know that his ghost always comes when the cheque of a dead man is cashed? Ask any banker,' he said, turning to the detective. 'Ask anyone at the Bank of England or any bank in the country. They all know the story of the ghost in the Bank of England.'

The police asked hundreds of questions that day and they heard the same story from everyone in the bank. Finally, they had to believe it and in the evening I was a free man.

The Italian's Story

Catherine Crowe, 1859

This is the story of my family, the Ferraldis. It is a very old Italian family and my story begins in 1550, in Florence, which was an important business centre at that time. Jacopo Ferraldi was a very rich man. He kept all his money under the floor in his house and was only happy when he was counting it. He was always afraid of thieves and so he had no friends and only two servants. One day he found that £2,000 was missing. To him this was not a lot of money but he was very angry and told his servants to leave.

Not long after this, a letter arrived from his sister, who lived in England. In the letter she said that her husband was dead and that her son, Arthur Allen, was coming to Florence to try to make some money for the family, who were now very poor. Jacopo was angry. He did not want his nephew to come, but when the young man arrived his anger changed to happiness. The young man had £2,000 with him and Jacopo decided to steal it.

That night, while they were having dinner, Jacopo murdered his nephew and hid his body under the floor. He counted the money happily, but the next night, when he sat down to dinner, Jacopo saw the ghost of his nephew in the chair opposite him. This happened every night at dinner-time and he started to feel more and more uncomfortable.

He counted the money happily.

He decided that the only way to stop the ghost coming was to travel to England and pay back the £2,000 to his sister. Of course, he could not leave the rest of his money at home, so he put it all into big boxes and took it with him. After weeks of travelling, Jacopo arrived at his sister's house in England. Two servants carried his boxes into the house and from their heaviness they guessed that the boxes were full of money.

Jacopo gave £2,000 to his sister, but of course he told her nothing about her son's death. 'I'm afraid he never arrived in Florence,' he said. He did not see the ghost again, but his next worry was his money. He was sure that the servants were planning to steal it. He was right. That night they came to Jacopo's room, murdered him and took the boxes. The next morning, a neighbour found the empty boxes at the side of the road. The police searched the servants' rooms, but they found nothing. They questioned the servants, but it seemed that they really had no idea about the money. It was gone.

Two hundred and fifty years later, I, Francesco Ferraldi, was born in the house of Jacopo Ferraldi in Florence. As I grew up, I felt that it was an unhappy house, and when I was older, my parents told me the story of the murder of Arthur Allen. They were very ashamed of Jacopo Ferraldi and no one in the family ever said his name. Every time I went into the room where Jacopo killed his nephew and hid his body, I was sure I could hear strange cries and screams.

A few years later, because my family was poor, I travelled to England to try to make some money. I was a good singer, so I went to all the rich people's houses in London and sang at parties for money. At one of these parties, a kind old man, Mr Greathead, heard me and asked me to stay at his house in the country for the summer. 'I would like you to sing at all my parties and to give lessons to my daughters,' he said. I was very happy to agree.

When I arrived Mr Greathead showed me round the house and garden. When we came to the flower garden, I was surprised to see a small part of it covered in Italian flowers.

'How do they grow here?' I asked. 'I've never seen them outside Italy.'

'I think the ground is very rich here,' said Mr Greathead. 'But, funnily enough, my wife and I have a disagreement about this part of the garden. I would like to make the house bigger by building here, but my wife won't agree. She says she saw the ghost here once.'

That night at dinner I asked Mrs Greathead about the ghost in the flower garden. 'I really *did* see someone or something there,' she said. 'It was an old man. He was very thin and he was holding a pencil and paper. He was walking up and down between those Italian flowers and the tree. I got the idea that he was looking for something. I ran into the house but, of course, when my husband

'I really did *see* someone or something there,' Mrs Greathead said.

came out he could see no one. Some of the servants have seen him, they say, and the gardener says that, when he works in that part of the garden, the old man always appears. I've also heard stories of a murder here many years ago.'

Mr Greathead did not believe his wife's story and a few weeks later work began on that part of the garden. One of the men found an old coin and gave it to Mr Greathead, who showed it to me in great excitement.

'Look,' he said. 'It's in Italian, isn't it? And look at the date — 1545. How strange.'

The workmen found many more coins that day, and at dinner Mrs Greathead was very excited. 'You see,' she said to her husband, 'now you must believe me. All that money belonged to the old man I saw. Perhaps he hid it under the ground and then someone murdered him. Now his ghost is looking for the money.'

I began to think about Jacopo Ferraldi. Could it be? I thought. But no, it was impossible.

After dinner we had coffee in the library and I told the Greatheads my old family story about Jacopo and the murder of his nephew. As we talked I noticed something like a map, hanging on the wall. 'This looks very old,' I said. 'And . . . how strange . . . some of the words are in Italian.' As I looked closer I saw that it was in fact a map of the garden. I could see the flower garden and between the Italian flowers and the tree there was a cross. Mr Greathead came to look too.

'Yes,' he said, 'we think the gardens were designed by an Italian . . . but what's wrong?'

I was looking at the back of the map, where I saw the words 'Jacopo Ferraldi' and the date '1550'. Then I was sure. I was in the same house that the old murderer, Jacopo Ferraldi, came to all those years ago. The cross on the map showed the place where all his money was under the ground. I believe that he guessed the servants were planning to rob him, so he hid the money in the garden to keep it safe. His ghost has walked there ever since, guarding our family's money.

The Greatheads were very surprised and pleased, especially Mrs Greathead, who loved to be right. They were very happy to give all the old coins to me, which I sold for enough money to make me a very rich man.

ACTIVITIES

The Dead Man of Varley Grange and **The Ghost Detective**

Before you read

1 Find these word in your dictionary:

cash (v)   *servant*

Which of them is

   a something you do with a cheque?

   b a job?

   Write a sentence using both words.

2 Do you believe in ghosts? If not, do you know anybody who does?
   Why do some people believe in ghosts, do you think?

After you read

3 In 'The Dead Man of Varley Grange', why does Dennis Varley kill
   his sister?

4 How many people see the ghost of Varley's sister?

5 In pairs, imagine and act out this conversation between Jack
   Darent and the writer at the beginning of the story.

   Student A: You are the writer. You don't want Jack to go to Varley
                  Grange. Think of reasons. Explain them to him.

   Student B: You are Jack Darent. Don't get angry. Tell your friend
                  that you will be fine.

6 Look at these sentences about 'The Ghost Detective'. Correct the
   ones that are not true.

   a James Loxley worries about the money on Christmas Day.

   b Martha Loxley sees her husband's ghost twice.

   c Susan says she took the money out of Loxley's coat pocket.

The Dream and **The Man with Two Shadows**

Before you read

7 Find these words in your dictionary.

   God   hell   moth

   Match them to these descriptions.

   a It flies around bright lights at night.

   b It's a place where no one wants to go.

c Religious people believe that he made the world.

8 What makes shadows? Is it unusual to have two shadows? Why, or why not?

After you read

9 Which of these belong in which story?

a picture on the wall   a hole in the floor   a murder
a love story   a man who comes back to life   a ship   children

10 In 'The Dream', why does the doctor think that Pat Connell is a lucky man?

11 At the end of the story, Pat's wife sees two people leaving the room. Who are they?

12 In 'The Man with Two Shadows', which people sometimes feel

a worried?

b jealous?

c angry?

What are their reasons for feeling like this?

The Ghost in the Bank of England and **The Italian's Story**

Before you read

13 Find these words in your dictionary.

banknote   cashier   nephew   scar

Use three of these words to complete these sentences.

Aunt Jo gave a . . . . . to her . . . . . for his birthday.

He took it to the bank and gave it to the . . . .

Write a sentence using the fourth word.

After you read

14 In 'The Ghost in the Bank of England', which two people go to prison? Why?

15 The date on the cheque and on the letter is 12th September. Mendez dies on the 11th September. Is this mystery explained at the end of the story? If not, what is your explanation?

16 These things happen in 'The Italian's Story'. Put them in the right order.

a Francesco sees Italian flowers in an English garden.

b Francesco studies a map.

c A ghost visits Jacopo at the dinner table.

d Jacopo takes all his money to England.

How are they important to the story?

17 Work in pairs. Imagine and act out a conversation between a policeman and Jacopo Ferraldi. Jacopo's nephew has disappeared.

Student A: You are Jacopo Ferraldi. You have murdered your nephew. You say that he never arrived at your house.

Student B: You are a policeman. Jacopo's neighbours say they saw a young man arriving from England.

18 Does the writer see the ghost in any of the stories in this book? If not, who sees the ghost?

Writing

19 Choose *two* of the things below. Say how important they are in *two* of the six stories:

a money   **b** murder   **c** pictures on the wall   **d** doctors

20 It is your job to sell Varley Grange, the old house in the first story, for a good price. Write an advertisement, describing the house and its history. Say why it is a wonderful place to live.

21 You are Wilson in 'The Ghost in the Bank of England'. You have just read the letter from Julius Mendez, with the cheque for £1,000. Write Mendez a letter of thanks. Say that you enjoyed working for him in Jamaica. Describe your life in England now and talk about your plans for the money.

22 In 'The Italian's Story', the servants come to Jacopo's room, murder him and take the boxes, but they do not find the money. Write the story of what Jacopo does with the money that night.

The Portrait of a Lady

HENRY JAMES

Level 3

Retold by Janet McAlpin

Series Editors: andy Hopkins and Jocelyn Potter

Contents

Introduction

'I thank you more than I can say, my lord, but I am not sure I want to marry anyone.'

This is how Isabel Archer answers Lord Warburton when he first asks her to marry him. Isabel is an intelligent young American woman whose father has just died. Her aunt, Mrs Touchett, invites her to visit Europe. In England she meets her rich uncle and her cousin Ralph. Two other rich men, Caspar Goodwood and Lord Warburton, would like to marry her but Isabel wants to travel, to meet new people and to learn about the world. She and her cousin Ralph become good friends. When Ralph's father dies, Isabel is surprised to learn that he has left her a lot of money: seventy thousand pounds.

When staying in Italy with her aunt, Isabel meets an American art lover, Gilbert Osmond. He is not rich, so she agrees to marry him, believing that her money can help him. Too late, she realizes that she has made a bad mistake. Osmond only cares about her money and doesn't really love her. He tries to get his daughter Pansy to marry Lord Warburton because he is rich and famous, knowing that Pansy is already happily in love with a younger man. When Isabel realizes Osmond's plan, she says that she will not help him and this makes Osmond very angry. By the end of the story Isabel understands who her real friends are. She is a sadder but wiser young lady.

Henry James was an American, born in New York in 1843. His father was a well-known writer and his brother, William James, was a famous university teacher. As a young man, James spent a lot of time travelling in Europe and he also studied law at Harvard University. He wrote his first stories in 1865. He moved to England in 1876 and decided to stay there but he also continued to make visits to France and Italy.

He lived in the small town of Rye on the south coast and became friends with many famous writers, among them Joseph Conrad, Ford Madox Ford and H. G. Wells. In 1915, James decided to become British. The King of England gave him the Order of Merit (a title which the king or queen gives to people who are successful in different areas of national life). James died the following year.

Henry James wrote many famous books, among them *Washington Square* (1880), *The Bostonians* (1886), *What Maisie Knew* (1887), *The Wings of a Dove* (1902), *The Ambassadors* (1903), and *The Golden Bowl* (1904). He started to write *The Portrait of a Lady* in 1880, when he was staying for some months in Florence. The book was immediately successful, both in Britain and the United States.

Henry James was interested in the way that people think and feel. The people he wrote about were usually people with plenty of money, who liked to travel around the world. He liked to describe young Americans visiting Europe and making friends with Europeans. The Americans in his stories are usually open-hearted and the Europeans are often clever, selfish and mainly interested in money. In this story, the dishonest people, Gilbert Osmond and Madame Merle, are in fact Americans but Americans who have liked in Europe for many years. The fortune which Ralph asks his father to give Isabel does not make her freer. In fact, it is the reason why Gilbert Osmond wants to marry her. He is not interested in her as a person: 'She has too many ideas.' Isabel wants to use her money to help other people and this is mainly why she agrees to marry Osmond.

Love, marriage, friendship and money are the things that lie at the heart of this story. With these important subjects, it is not surprising that *The Portrait of a Lady* is one of Henry James's best-loved books.

Chapter 1   Isabel's Two Visitors

One wet spring afternoon Isabel Archer had two visitors. The first was an old lady in a big raincoat. Isabel did not know her. She put down the book that she was reading and stood up.

'I guess you're one of my sister's daughters,' said the stranger.

'Ah,' said Isabel slowly, 'then I guess you're our bad Aunt Lydia.'

'Yes, I am your aunt,' said the woman, 'but I'm not bad. Did your father say that? He didn't like me. We never spoke again after your mother died. Which daughter are you?'

'I'm Isabel, the youngest,' said Isabel.

'And are you the prettiest?'

'I have no idea,' said Isabel.

'I'm sure you are.'

And in that way, Isabel and her aunt made friends.

They talked for an hour, about Isabel's two married sisters, about their father, and about the house. Isabel and her sisters were selling the house.

'We can't keep it,' explained Isabel, 'because father didn't leave much money when he died. But I'm sorry. This was my grandmother's house, and I love it.'

'I don't see why,' said her aunt. 'Your father died here.'

'A great many people have died here,' said Isabel, 'and a great many people have lived here. This old house is full of past times. That's why I like it.'

'If you like the past you must leave America,' said her aunt. 'Come to Italy. That's where I live. My house in Florence is very, very old.'

'Florence?' said Isabel. 'Don't you live in England?'

'My husband lives in England and I live in Florence,' said Isabel's aunt. 'You shall see both. Leave it to me.'

When her aunt returned to her hotel, Isabel tried to return to her book, but her thoughts were everywhere. She was very happy in America, but she also wanted to see Europe. She was more serious and intelligent than her sisters, and she wanted to learn as much as possible.

Some time later, her second visitor arrived. This time, Isabel was not surprised. Caspar Goodwood lived in Boston, but his business often brought him to New York. He always wrote a letter before he came. He thought Isabel was the most beautiful young woman of her time.

And Caspar Goodwood was the finest young man that Isabel knew. He was tall and strong, like a soldier, perhaps a little too square, but handsome and brown. When he came into the room his blue eyes were full of hope. Isabel could see that he wanted to speak of marriage, but after half an hour she sent him away. When he left, he was not smiling.

Chapter 2   Tea in an English Garden

In summer, Mr Touchett liked to take afternoon tea in his garden. He drank it very slowly. His cup was big, with bright colours, and very old – much older than Mr Touchett. Not far away, his son Ralph walked with Lord Warburton. They were smoking cigarettes. Two dogs watched the men.

Ralph Touchett loved his father. They were American, but Ralph was a small boy when his father came to live in England. At that time Mr Touchett worked for an American bank. He was an old man now – old, and sick, and very rich, but he didn't want to return to America. He loved his old English house with its great garden.

His wife did not love England. Did she love Mr Touchett? It was difficult to say. She certainly loved her son Ralph, and they spent three months of every year together. Ralph was sick too. In the summer he stayed in England with his father. In the winter he visited his mother in Florence. Ralph needed the sun.

Ralph was speaking to Lord Warburton about his cousin. 'Her name is Isabel,' he said. 'My mother has just arrived with her from America. Look, here she comes.'

Isabel came out of the house and Ralph went to meet her. The smaller dog ran up to her. She picked it up and smiled. 'Is this your little dog?' she asked Ralph.

'He was,' said Ralph, 'but I think he loves you now.'

Isabel smiled again. 'Your mother is in her room,' she said. 'Can you please go to her at seven o'clock?'

'Of course,' said Ralph. 'Now please come and meet my father and our neighbour, Lord Warburton.'

'My dear,' said Mr Touchett, 'you must have some tea. Where is my wife?'

'She is in her room, Daddy,' said Ralph.

'Then perhaps I'll see her at dinner,' said his father.

Isabel sat down with the little dog. Her dress was black because her father was dead, but her eyes were bright and quick. 'How perfect it is here,' she said, 'the river, the garden, your beautiful old house . . .'

'Miss Archer,' said Lord Warburton, 'if you like old places you must visit my house.'

Isabel asked about his family. Lord Warburton had two younger brothers and four sisters. Both his parents were dead. One brother was a soldier and the other was in the church. 'They're all good people,' he explained. 'Not specially clever, but pleasant and good.' Isabel agreed to meet his sisters.

A man brought Lord Warburton's horse and Ralph went to

'You once wanted to know my idea of an interesting woman,'
Lord Warburton said to Ralph. 'Well there it is.'

say goodbye. Lord Warburton looked back at Isabel. 'You once wanted to know my idea of an interesting woman,' Lord Warburton said to Ralph. 'Well, there it is.'

Chapter 3   Mrs Touchett's Plans for Isabel

At seven o'clock Ralph went to his mother's room. She was dressed for dinner. She kissed him and asked about her husband's health. Then she asked about Ralph's health. The news was not very good about either of them.

'It's the English weather,' said Mrs Touchett. 'That's why I live in Florence.'

Ralph smiled. 'I'll come to Italy in the winter, dear mother,' he said. 'Now tell me about the young lady. What will you do with her?'

'I want her to stay here for a month. Then I will take her to Paris. She needs clothes to wear in Florence.'

'Of course,' said Ralph. 'But I mean, what will you do with her in a more general way?'

'I will show her four European countries and she will learn perfect French. She already knows it very well.'

Ralph said, 'That sounds very dry.'

Mrs Touchett laughed. 'If it's dry, Isabel will water it. She is like a summer rain.'

'She is certainly very natural,' said Ralph. 'Where did you find this pretty cousin who I never knew about?'

Mrs Touchett told him. Then she asked, 'Do you think her so very pretty?'

'Very pretty,' said Ralph. 'And Warburton thinks she is interesting, too.'

His mother shook her head. 'Lord Warburton won't understand her. He needn't try.'

'He's very intelligent,' said Ralph. 'What does Isabel know about English lords?'

'Nothing,' said Mrs Touchett. 'But she will enjoy learning.'

Ralph laughed and looked out of the window. 'There's still time before dinner,' he said. 'Tell me some more. Won't Isabel give you trouble?'

'I hope not,' said Mrs Touchett. 'But the money question is a little difficult. She doesn't want my help, so she thinks she is going to pay her travel costs.'

'Ah, she's not rich,' said Ralph, 'but she likes to be independent. How interesting. Will you find her a husband?'

'Certainly not,' said Mrs Touchett. 'She is quite able to do that for herself.'

'Perhaps she has already chosen,' said Ralph.

'I don't know about a husband,' said Mrs Touchett, 'but there's a young man in Boston . . .'

'Come down to dinner now,' said Ralph. He didn't want to know about the young man in Boston.

Chapter 4   Getting to Know Lord Warburton

Isabel loved Gardencourt. Her uncle's old English house seemed like a picture from a book.

'It's a dear old place,' said Ralph, 'but I'm afraid it's very quiet for you. My father cannot leave his chair.'

The old man was very kind to Isabel. She often sat with him, asking questions about England and Queen Victoria. She wanted to know about the English people.

'Will I feel at home here?' she asked. 'Are they kind to young women?'

'I don't know about young women in the lower class, but I think women in the other classes are comfortable.'

'Goodness! How many classes are there?'

'I'm not sure,' said Mr Touchett. 'That's why it's good to be an American here. You don't belong to any class.'

Sometimes she took a boat on the river with Ralph, and sometimes they walked, but not far, because Ralph was not strong. He liked talking, but he was never serious.

One day, Isabel said angrily, 'You don't care for England, you don't care for America, what *do* you care for?'

'I care for nothing but you, dear cousin,' said Ralph, with a big smile.

Lord Warburton came to Gardencourt again, and stayed one night. 'Ralph is so lazy,' he said to Isabel. 'I am glad to see that he takes you boating.'

'Oh no,' laughed Ralph. 'I don't take Isabel – she takes *me*. My cousin does everything well, specially boating.'

Isabel asked Lord Warburton a great many questions too, and he answered them very carefully. Isabel was amused. 'He thinks I'm a wild thing, and that I've never seen forks and spoons,' she thought. In fact Lord Warburton knew more about the United States than Isabel. He was interesting and intelligent and kind.

When he left, Isabel said, 'I like your English lord very much.'

'So do I,' said Ralph. 'I love him. But I pity him more. He was born a lord, but he thinks this is wrong. He has modern ideas, but he can't change anything. You'll see, when we visit him at Lockleigh.'

The next week, Ralph and Mrs Touchett took her there. Lord Warburton showed Isabel his house, and she met his shy sisters. She realized that this great house belonged to a very old family, and Lord Warburton was its head.

Chapter 5   Henrietta Comes to Stay

When they returned to Gardencourt there was a letter waiting. Isabel showed it to her uncle. 'It's from my friend Henrietta,' she said. 'She writes for a newspaper in New York and they have sent her to London. She wants to see me.'

'Please ask her to visit us,' said Mr Touchett.

Isabel did so, but she wasn't sure it was a good idea. Henrietta Stackpole was the most independent woman that Isabel knew. She was not married, and had very little money, but she had a job, and she paid for her poor sister's children to go to school. Isabel admired her friend very much, but she didn't want her to write about Gardencourt and the Touchett family for her newspaper.

'So, she is a modern American woman,' said Ralph, while they were waiting at the station for Henrietta's train from London. 'Will I like her or will I dislike her?'

'It doesn't matter,' said Isabel. 'She doesn't care what men think of her.'

'Do you think she will write about us all for her newspaper?'

'I'll ask her not to,' Isabel answered.

'Then you think it's possible?'

'Perfectly.'

'Ah well, I think I will dislike her,' said Ralph.

'You'll probably fall in love with her at the end of three days.'

'And see my love letters in her newspaper? Never!'

But when Henrietta arrived, Ralph saw that she was a fresh, fair person with brave eyes and a high, clear voice, and he found it difficult not to like her at once.

Over the next few days, Ralph had many conversations with Henrietta. She spent the mornings writing in her room, and in the afternoons they walked together in the garden.

*When Henrietta arrived, Ralph saw that she was a fresh,
fair person with brave eyes and a high clear voice.*

'Do you people think of yourselves as American or English?' she asked him. 'I need to know how to talk to you.'

'Please talk to us anyway,' laughed Ralph.

'Do you always spend your time like this?'

'I don't usually spend it so pleasantly.'

'You know what I mean – you have no job.'

'Ah,' said Ralph, 'I'm the laziest man alive.'

'Why not go home to America?' said Henrietta. 'Find something to do – some new idea, some big work.'

'Isn't that very difficult?'

'Not if you put your heart into it.'

'Ah, my heart,' said Ralph.

'Haven't you got a heart?'

'I had one a few days ago, but I've lost it since.'

'Don't be funny,' said Henrietta.

♦

One morning, Henrietta showed her work to Isabel. 'Can I read this to you?' she said. 'I have written about Gardencourt.'

'I didn't want you to do that,' said Isabel.

Henrietta looked at her with clear eyes. 'Why, it's just what the people at home want, and it's a beautiful place.'

'It's too beautiful to go in the newspapers, and it's not what my uncle wants.'

'Then I won't do it,' said Henrietta, 'but it's a pity. Now Isabel, I have something to tell you. Caspar Goodwood is here too. We travelled on the same boat from America.'

'I know,' said Isabel. His letter was in her pocket. 'Dear Miss Archer,' it said, 'I have come to England. I cannot stay in America when you are not there. Can I see you again for half an hour? This is my dearest wish.'

Isabel could not decide how to answer this letter.

Chapter 6   Two Men with One Question

Lord Warburton soon visited Gardencourt again. It was a beautiful day, and he found Isabel in the garden. He wore a happy smile, and was ready to walk, or sit, or do anything that Isabel wanted to do.

He was also ready to do something which would surprise his friends. He knew a lot about Isabel's country, but very little about her family. She was not rich, and not the most beautiful woman that he knew. He counted no more than twenty-six hours with her since they met. But he cared nothing for these thoughts. He wanted to ask Isabel to marry him.

Isabel did not want to hear this question. She liked him, and she knew he would make a good husband. He was kind and honest. Why then did she hope he would not ask?

While she waited, Isabel touched the letter in her pocket. She liked Caspar very much too – a strong young man from her brave young country. England was not her country, and its rich old families had many rules. 'Can I ever be happy with an English lord?' she asked herself.

At last Lord Warburton asked his question.

'I thank you more than I can say, my lord,' said Isabel slowly, 'but I am not sure I want to marry anyone.'

'Oh, Miss Archer,' said Lord Warburton. 'Give me some hope. Please think it over for as long as you wish.'

'I will,' said Isabel, 'but please don't hope too much.'

After three days she wrote to him. 'You are very kind,' she said, 'but I cannot change my answer.'

She told her uncle, and he told her aunt. Mrs Touchett said, 'Do you hope to do something better?'

'I'm not sure of that,' said Isabel smiling. 'I just don't love Lord Warburton enough to marry him.'

'You did right to say no, then,' said Mrs Touchett.

◆

Soon it was time for Henrietta to return to London. She asked Isabel to go with her for a few days, and Ralph decided to go with them. Mr Touchett had a house in Winchester Square, but it was closed and cold, so they stayed in a hotel.

The three young people visited famous places in London – the British Museum more than once, the Tower of London, Westminster Abbey, and Kew Gardens.

On the third day, Isabel could see that Ralph was tired. 'Henrietta is busy with another friend tonight,' she said, 'so I will have a quiet dinner in my room.'

'Why can't I eat with you?' asked Ralph. 'Do you have another friend to see too?'

'No,' said Isabel. 'But you need to rest, and so do I.'

To her surprise, a visitor did come to see her in the hotel that evening. It was Caspar Goodwood.

'Why didn't you answer my letter?' he asked quickly.

'How did you know I was here?' replied Isabel, calmly.

'Henrietta told me. Can I stay?'

'You can sit down, certainly. Why are you here?'

'To follow you. I don't want to lose you.'

'You cannot lose what is not yours,' said Isabel.

'Why didn't you write to me,' he asked again.

Isabel said, 'I thought it was the best thing. I don't want you to think of me. Be strong.'

'I am strong,' said the young man, 'and that's why I love you more strongly.'

Isabel was silent. At last she said, 'Then think of me, but don't see me for a year or two. Don't follow me.'

'I'm not sure of that,' said Isabel smiling. 'I just don't
love Lord Warburton enough to marry him.'

'If I do that,' he replied, 'when will you marry me? That's the only question.'

'Probably never,' said Isabel. 'I really don't want to marry, or to talk about it. I must be independent.'

Chapter 7   Mysterious Madame Marle

When Ralph and Isabel returned to Gardencourt, Mr Touchett's health was worse. The days passed. Mrs Touchett did not speak of leaving for Paris.

There was another visitor in the house, a friend of Mrs Touchett's. When she first met Madame Merle, Isabel thought she was French, but she looked German with her thick fair hair and her large white hands.

'I'm American,' she told Isabel, 'but my husband was Swiss. Now I live in Rome.' In fact, Madame Merle had very little money, and liked to stay with rich friends like Mrs Touchett, who admired her greatly.

Isabel admired her too. Madame Merle talked well about books and pictures, and played the piano beautifully.

'I hope the music helps my uncle to feel better,' Isabel said to Ralph. 'Madame Merle plays so beautifully.'

'She does everything beautifully,' said Ralph.

Isabel looked at her cousin carefully. 'You don't like her,' she guessed.

Ralph's answer was strange. 'I loved her once,' he said, 'when her husband was alive.'

They did not speak about Madame Merle again. Ralph stayed with his father as much as he could. One day they spoke about money. 'I don't need a lot, Daddy,' said Ralph.

'Well, you'll have enough,' said Mr Touchett. 'Enough for two. The best thing that you can do, when I'm gone, is to marry.'

Madame Merle played the piano beautifully.

Ralph said nothing, and his father said softly. 'What do you think of your cousin?'

Ralph was silent for a long time. Then he said, 'I like Isabel very much, but I can't be in love with her because she's my cousin, and because I'm a sick man.'

'If you won't marry,' said Mr Touchett, 'what will you do when I'm not here to take care of? The bank does not interest you. What are your interests?'

Ralph answered his father carefully. 'I take a great interest in my cousin,' he said, 'but not the sort of interest that you want. I will not live for many years, but I hope I'll live long enough to see what Isabel does with her life. She is very independent. She does not need me. But I would like to do something for her, Daddy. I would like her to be rich.'

'I'll do anything that you like,' said Mr Touchett, 'but I'm not sure it's right. Isabel's a sweet young thing, but if she is rich, will she be sensible?'

'She will do good things with the money,' said Ralph.

♦

Soon it was too cold to sit in the garden. Madame Merle spent her days writing letters, painting pictures, and playing the piano. To Isabel she seemed a wise woman of the world, but sometimes she said surprising things.

'I'd love to be your age again,' she said one day, 'to have my life before me again . . .'

'Your life is still before you,' said Isabel, sweetly.

'No. The best part has gone. I have no husband, no child, no fortune, and I am not beautiful now.'

'You have many friends, dear lady.'

'I am not so sure!' said Madame Merle.

♦

When she was not talking with her new friend, Isabel spent her time reading in the library. The house was very quiet. One afternoon she looked up to see Ralph in the doorway.

'It's finished,' he said. 'My dear father died an hour ago.'

'Ah, my poor Ralph!' said Isabel, putting out her two hands to him.

Chapter 8   Pansy and her Father

Six months later, on one of the first days of May, a small group of people sat in a beautiful room in a house on a hill above Florence. A young girl was looking at a picture.

A man watched her. 'Well, my dear, what do you think of it?' he asked, speaking in Italian.

'It's very pretty, Papa,' said the girl. 'Did you do paint it?'

'Certainly,' said the man. 'Don't you think I'm clever?'

Papa was forty, with a fine head and intelligent eyes. His thick hair was short and grey, and he wore a tidy beard.

The girl smiled at him sweetly. 'I, too, can paint pictures, Papa,' she said, and she looked across the room to where two nuns were sitting.

'She can paint very well,' said the older nun, in French, 'and she can play the piano.'

'Go into the garden,' said the father, also in French, 'and bring some flowers.' When the girl left, he said to the nuns, 'She's really very pretty. Is she good?'

'Oh yes, Monsieur,' said the younger nun. 'She's perfect. We love her too much. Pansy is like a daughter to us – she was so small when she came to us.'

'I do not want to take her away from you,' said the man.

'We're happy to hear that. Fifteen is very young.'

71

'I would like her to be with you always,' continued the man. 'But now, perhaps, I must have her with me.'

'Ah Monsieur,' said the older nun, smiling and standing up. 'She is good, but she is for the world, not for us.'

Pansy returned with two bunches of roses, one white and the other red. She gave them to the nuns with a kiss. They were saying goodbye when a new visitor came into the room.

The man looked surprised, but stood still and said nothing. The young girl gave a soft little cry: 'Ah, Madame Merle!'

'Yes, it's Madame Merle. I've come to welcome you home,' said the visitor, and she held out two hands to the girl.

'These ladies have brought my daughter home and now they are returning to Rome,' the man explained.

'I have just come from Rome,' said Madame Merle. 'It's very beautiful there now.'

'She came to see me at school,' Pansy told her father.

'Madame Merle is a good friend to us,' he explained to the nuns. 'She will help us to decide if my daughter can return to you in Rome at the end of the holidays.'

'I decide nothing,' laughed Madame Merle. 'I know your school is good, but it is expensive, and Mr Osmond must of course remember that Miss Osmond is for the world.'

'That's what I told monsieur,' said the older nun.

'Am I not for you, Papa?' asked Pansy in her clear, soft voice.

Osmond laughed. 'For me and for the world, Pansy.'

The nuns left, Pansy returned to the garden, and Madame Merle now spoke to Osmond in English.

'I've been in Florence for a week – at Palazzo Crescentini with Mrs Touchett. I hoped you would visit me.'

'I didn't know you were there.'

'It's not important to me, but perhaps it will be important to you. When did you last make a new friend?'

'You were the last. I don't want new friends.'

*Pansy returned with two bunches of roses, one white
and the other red.*

'You're too lazy, Gilbert. It is time for you to meet another. Her name is Isabel Archer. She's American. Mrs Touchett is her aunt.'

'And why must I meet Miss Archer? Is she beautiful, clever, rich and good?'

'She's young – twenty-three years old. I like her a lot. Yes, she is beautiful and intelligent, and, for an American, she comes from a good family.'

'And is she rich?'

'Mr Touchett left her seventy thousand pounds.'

Chapter 9   Isabel Meets Gilbert Osmond

When Mr Touchett died, Mrs Touchett sold his London house. Ralph kept Gardencourt but he soon left England to spend the winter in Italy.

Mrs Touchett was surprised to learn about Isabel's fortune. She told her friend Madame Merle.

'Ah, the clever girl,' said Madame Merle.

Mrs Touchett gave her a quick look. 'What do you mean?'

Madame Merle dropped her eyes. 'I mean it's clever to get a fortune without trying,' she said.

'She certainly didn't try,' said Mrs Touchett. 'It was Ralph's idea. She never knew of it.'

And that was true. At first Isabel couldn't understand how rich she was. 'Is it good for me?' she asked her aunt.

'It can't be bad for you,' said Mrs Touchett. 'Of course you don't have to stay with your boring old aunt now. Perhaps you can ask Miss Stackpole to travel with you.'

'I don't think you're boring,' Isabel replied to this, and they agreed to travel together to Paris and Italy.

Henrietta was not ready to leave England, but she planned

to visit Europe soon, with some friends. She knew that Caspar Goodwood was now back in America. 'I hope you gave him some hope for the future,' she said to Isabel.

'I asked Mr Goodwood not to speak about marriage,' said Isabel, 'and I must ask you the same, Henrietta.'

'Isabel Archer,' said her friend, seriously, 'if you marry one of these people I'll never speak to you again.'

Isabel thought of Lord Warburton, and smiled to herself. She had said no to 'one of these people', but she certainly didn't want Henrietta to know that.

The two friends said goodbye, and agreed to meet again in Italy.

◆

Isabel and her aunt visited Paris, and then joined Ralph in Florence. There, in Mrs Touchett's old and beautiful house, Isabel also met Madame Merle again, and when Gilbert Osmond came to visit Madame Merle, Isabel met him too. He asked her to visit his house on the hill, to meet his daughter and to take tea in the garden.

Isabel enjoyed the visit. While Madame Merle sat in the garden with Pansy, Osmond showed Isabel all his beautiful things. 'I, too, am American,' he explained, 'but I like the old world. I like fine old things. I'm not rich, so I cannot buy much, but what I buy is always perfect.'

After that visit, Gilbert Osmond came often to Palazzo Crescentini. 'Do you think he wants to marry Isabel?' asked Mrs Touchett. 'He has only a few fine pictures and a pretty daughter.'

'Isabel likes the poor child,' said Madame Merle.

'The child can't hope to marry without a fortune,' said Mrs Touchett. 'Isabel is kind – I hope she is careful too.'

Isabel was happy in Florence, but sometimes her thoughts

went back to two men, Caspar Goodwood and Lord Warburton. She hoped they were not unhappy, and pictured them with better wives than she could ever be. She did not realize that she would see one of them again soon.

Chapter 10   Choosing a Husband

In the same way that he once wanted Isabel to see London, now Ralph wanted her to see Rome. They decided to go there to meet Henrietta and her friends.

'You'll like Rome,' said Gilbert Osmond when Isabel told him her plans. 'I'd like to see you there.'

'Then why don't you come with us?' said Isabel.

'Perhaps I will,' said Osmond. 'Perhaps I'll join you there. First I must ask someone to take care of Pansy.'

After Isabel and Ralph left Florence, Osmond told Madame Merle about this conversation.

'She wants me to go to Rome with her,' he said in a low voice.

'I'm glad to hear it. Of course you'll go.'

'Ah,' said Osmond. 'You want me to work hard for this plan of yours.'

'I'm sure you enjoy it,' said Madame Merle with a smile.

'I do like her,' said Osmond.

'Good.'

'But there's just one problem. She has too many ideas.'

'Ah yes, she is clever.'

'The ideas must stop,' said Osmond.

Madame Merle looked at him and said nothing. Then he said, 'If I go to Rome what will I do with Pansy?'

'I'll go and see her,' said Madame Merle.

♦

'You'll like Rome,' said Gilbert Osmond when Isabel told
him her plans. 'I'd like to see you there.'

Lord Warburton was in Rome. He found Isabel one afternoon while she was resting on a stone in the Forum. The sky was blue and clear, and when she looked up she saw him.

'Lord Warburton!' she said, standing up.

'I didn't know you were here,' he said. 'I was travelling in the East – Turkey and Greece. Now I'm returning to England. Can I sit down?'

'I'm with my cousin,' said Isabel. 'He's over there with some friends. Please wait for him.'

It was difficult to talk. Lord Warburton was clearly unhappy. When Ralph and Henrietta came, it was easier. The two men were very pleased to be together again. Lord Warburton met the other people in their little group, and then he walked away with Ralph.

'Who is the older man?' Lord Warburton asked Ralph.

'His name's Gilbert Osmond – he lives in Florence.'

'Does Isabel like him?'

'She's not sure yet.'

'Is he very clever?'

'Very,' said Ralph, and took his friend by the arm.

That evening they all went to the theatre. In the dark, Lord Warburton watched Isabel. He left early.

'Poor Lord Warburton,' said Isabel. 'He's a nice man.'

'He's very lucky,' said Osmond. 'A great lord, handsome, and Isabel likes him. Why do you call him poor?'

Ralph said, 'Women, after they hurt a man, often pity him. They think it is kind to do that.'

Osmond realized that the English lord loved Isabel.

Two days later, Lord Warburton met Isabel again. 'I'm leaving Rome,' he said, 'so I must say goodbye.'

Isabel was sorry to hear it, but she didn't say so.

'You don't care what I do,' said Lord Warburton, sadly. 'When will I see you again?'

Isabel was quiet, then she said, 'After you're married.'

'That will never be,' said Lord Warburton. 'It will be after you are married.' And they said goodbye.

Then Isabel had a letter from Mrs Touchett. 'Will you come back to Florence?' she asked. 'It is time to travel again. Do you want to come with me?'

Isabel replied quickly to say 'yes', and Ralph agreed to take her back to Florence the next day. That evening, in the rose-coloured sitting-room of their hotel, Isabel told Osmond about her plans to travel. She was going away for many months.

'Go everywhere, do everything, be happy,' said Osmond. 'But you'll be tired some day. Shall I wait until then to say what I want to say?'

'I don't know until you say it,' said Isabel, lightly.

He looked at the ground. 'I find I'm in love with you.'

'Ah,' said Isabel quickly. 'Keep that until I *am* tired.'

'No, hear it now,' said Osmond, looking up. 'I have little to give you. I have no fortune, and I'm not famous. But for me you're the most important woman in the world.'

'Please go now,' said Isabel. 'Goodnight.'

◆

One year later Isabel returned to Florence. In the late spring, she agreed to marry Gilbert Osmond.

Chapter 11   Caspar's Visit

Isabel told Caspar Goodwood first. She wrote to him in Boston, and he left immediately for Florence. By ship and train his journey took seventeen days. Caspar arrived late one night and went straight to see Isabel in the morning.

Caspar arrived late one night and went straight to see
Isabel in the morning.

'Are you very tired?' asked Isabel.

'I'm never tired,' said Caspar Goodwood. 'Now tell me, who and what is Mr Gilbert Osmond?'

'Who and what? Nobody and nothing but a good and quiet man. He's not in business, and he isn't rich or famous.'

'In your letter you say he's American. Doesn't he like the United States?'

'He never goes there. He's happy in Italy.'

'I thought you didn't want to marry.'

'No one can be more surprised than me,' she said slowly.

'You told me to wait two years.'

'I promised nothing. I was perfectly free.'

He was silent for quite some time. To change the subject, Isabel asked, 'Have you seen Henrietta Stackpole?'

'Yes,' said Goodwood. 'She's busy with her writing work in America, but I think she wants to see more of Europe. Does she know Mr Osmond?'

'A little,' said Isabel. 'And she doesn't like him. But of course I'm not marrying to please Henrietta.'

He was silent again for some time. 'Well,' he said at last. 'I've seen you, which is what I wanted. I will not trouble you again.' He went to the door, without shaking hands. At the door he stopped and said, 'I'll leave Florence tomorrow.' He was very calm, but she was not.

'I am glad to hear it,' she said. For some minutes after he left she did feel glad, then suddenly she began to cry.

♦

The next day, Isabel told her aunt. 'There is nothing *of* Osmond,' said Mrs Touchett, 'no money, no name, no importance. Don't you care for these things?'

Isabel said, 'I care very much for money, and that's why I want Mr Osmond to have some.'

'Give it to him then,' said her aunt, 'but don't marry him.'

Mrs Touchett told Ralph. He said nothing about it for three days. He was looking very sick, and sat quietly in the garden while Isabel went out walking with her lover. At last he said, 'I had great hopes for you, Isabel.'

Isabel didn't understand, and Ralph couldn't explain. He wanted Isabel's money to make her free. Now Isabel wanted to use the money to help Osmond. Isabel was warm and honest but Ralph thought Osmond was cold and small. He chose only perfect things and Isabel was just another perfect thing.

It was clear to Isabel that they did not like Gilbert Osmond, but she did not worry. She was not marrying him to please the Touchetts.

Pansy, now sixteen and a little taller, was more polite. 'You will be good for papa,' she said. 'You're both so quiet and so serious.'

'I'll be very kind to you, my good little Pansy,' said Isabel. And she was.

Soon after the marriage the family moved to a big house in Rome. A year later a baby was born, but the poor little boy died after six months. Isabel quietly watched Pansy grow up.

Chapter 12   Osmond's Plan for Pansy

When Pansy was nineteen she fell in love. She said nothing about it to her father, but Isabel knew. The young man was Ned Rosier, an American who lived in Paris. When he travelled to Rome, he always visited Isabel's 'evenings'.

'Mrs Osmond,' he said to Isabel, watching Pansy serve tea. 'You must help me. I want to marry Pansy. I have enough money.'

Isabel held her 'evenings' on Thursdays. Osmond asked only

the best people, but Isabel welcomed her old friends. Ned Rosier was the son of her father's friend.

'Your fortune is enough for Pansy, Mr Rosier,' she said, 'but I'm afraid it isn't large enough for her father.'

Isabel now knew that her marriage was not happy. Osmond thought she had too many ideas. He told her that one day. Too many ideas? Didn't married people like to talk about ideas? She began to understand that the only ideas Osmond wanted her to have were his ideas. He wanted to change her. He didn't want her to be strong and independent – he wanted her just to be pretty, like Pansy. But Isabel could not change. She realized that when she fell in love with Osmond she saw only half the man. Now she began to see all of him.

She said nothing to Ralph, though she knew he was right about Osmond. Ralph was staying in a hotel near her house. Osmond didn't like Isabel visiting Ralph in the hotel, but Ralph was very sick. Isabel was afraid he was dying.

'You really mustn't travel,' she said. 'Why did Lord Warburton agree to bring you here?'

'He knows I live only for you,' laughed Ralph, weakly.

Ralph was too sick to leave the hotel, but Lord Warburton came to the Osmonds' house every Thursday evening. He talked a lot to Pansy. Osmond was watching.

'Perhaps Lord Warburton wishes to marry Pansy,' he said.

Madame Merle said the same.

After her marriage, Isabel did not see much of Madame Merle. She was often away, but now she was in Rome again, and she was careful not to see the Osmonds too often.

'I am careful,' she told Isabel, 'because I don't want you to worry. Sometimes a husband's old friend can forget that his wife will worry if she thinks they are together too much.'

Isabel did not worry in this way, but one day she came into a room and saw them together. Madame Merle was standing, and Osmond was sitting. 'How strange,' thought Isabel. 'I know they're old friends, but Osmond is always very polite.'

'Ah, Isabel,' said Madame Merle, when she saw her. 'We're speaking of Pansy. Does Lord Warburton love her?'

'I don't know,' said Isabel, 'but Pansy does not love him.'

'Pansy will do as I say,' said Osmond. 'Lord Warburton loved you, Isabel, so I know you can help. Please do what you can. It will be a great marriage.'

Isabel thought about it and decided that she agreed. 'Pansy will be perfect at Lockleigh,' she said to herself, 'if Lord Warburton can be happy with her.' She wanted to be sure, so she asked her cousin, 'Is Lord Warburton in love?'

'Very much, I think,' said Ralph, 'but not with Pansy. If he wants to marry her, it's because he wants to be near you.'

Isabel was silent. Ralph watched her. He knew she was unhappy, and he knew she didn't like to speak of it. 'Ah, my dear Isabel,' he said at last. 'I wanted so much for you.'

She kissed him. 'You're my best friend,' she said.

Chapter 13   Madame Merle's Secret

One evening, Isabel took Pansy to a great party. Osmond stayed at home because he didn't like to dance. Pansy loved dancing, and Lord Warburton and Isabel sat watching her.

'I'm forty-two years old, Mrs Osmond,' he said. 'Will Pansy marry me?'

'She will wish to please her father,' said Isabel.

'Then I will send him my letter,' said Warburton. 'I wrote it today, but I wanted to speak to you first.'

Isabel smiled at Ned Rosier, who was standing near them. Lord Warburton followed her smile. 'Why does that man look so sad?' he asked.

'Ah, my dear Isabel,' he said at last. 'I wanted
so much for you.'

'Because he isn't rich and he isn't clever. But he cares for Pansy, and Pansy cares for him.'

Isabel saw the surprise on Lord Warburton's face, and changed the subject.

Three days later he came to tell the Osmonds that he was returning to England. Ralph was very sick, to sick to travel, but Lord Warburton knew that he wanted too die at Gardencourt. He said nothing of marriage to Pansy, and nothing to give Osmond hope for the future.

Osmond did not like Ralph, and was pleased he was leaving Rome. To Lord Warburton he was coldly polite. He called Pansy to say goodbye.

'I'm going away,' said Lord Warburton. 'And I want to tell you how much I hope you will be very happy.'

'Thank you, Lord Warburton,' said Pansy softly.

Looking at Isabel he said, 'I'm sure you will be happy – you've got a very good friend.' Pansy smiled sweetly and said goodbye.

He shook hands with Isabel silently, and soon he left.

Isabel knew Osmond was very angry, and waited for him to speak of it. He said to her at last, 'You've played a very deep game.'

'I've no idea what you mean,' Isabel replied.

'I thought Warburton wrote me a letter – that's what you told me.'

'That's what he told me.'

'Where is it then?'

'I've no idea. I didn't ask him.'

'I'm sure you stopped the letter,' said Osmond. 'I can't forgive you. Everyone will laugh at me now, because I tried to marry my daughter to a lord.' Isabel saw that he cared nothing for his daughter's happiness.

Osmond sent Pansy back to the nuns for a time. 'I want my

daughter to be fresh and soft,' he explained. 'Pansy's life is getting a little too fast – she needs to rest. I like to think of her in that old place. She will have her books, she can paint, and she will have her piano. I want her to have time to think.'

He never spoke about Warburton again, but Madame Merle did. 'What did you do to send Lord Warburton away?' she asked Isabel angrily. 'That was not kind to Pansy.'

'Pansy doesn't care for him. She's very glad he's gone,' said Isabel.

'I know he once asked you to marry him. Did you want to keep his love?' said Madame Merle. 'I wanted this marriage so much. Why did you stop us from having him?'

These words surprised Isabel. 'Who are you – what are you?' she asked in a quiet voice. 'What are you to my husband?'

'Everything,' replied Madame Merle. 'I made your marriage, and I wanted to make Pansy's too.'

'Why?' asked Isabel. 'What are you to us?'

'I am Pansy's mother,' said Madame Merle.

Chapter 14 'My Cousin Is Dying'

Isabel could not stop thinking about Madame Merle's words and her ugly secret. She realized that she knew nothing of the first Mrs Osmond – did she die before Pansy was born? When did Madame Merle's husband die? Why didn't Osmond marry her? She thought about how much Osmond loved money. Did Madame Merle choose Isabel for Osmond because of her fortune?

Mrs Touchett wrote to Isabel from Gardencourt: 'Ralph is near the end. He wants to see you if you are not too busy.' Isabel went immediately to her husband.

'I must go to Gardencourt,' she told him. 'My cousin is dying.'

'Your cousin was dying when we married,' said Osmond. 'He will continue to live.'

'I want to see him before he dies,' said Isabel.

'But I don't want you to go,' said her husband.

Isabel realized she must choose the right thing to do. She loved Ralph and she must see him, but Osmond was very angry. 'The world thinks we have a perfect marriage,' he said. 'If you go against my wishes, everyone will know it's not true. A marriage, Isabel, is a very important thing.'

Isabel agreed with this, but she said, 'I can see you're afraid I will not come back,' and she left the same night.

On her way to the train she visited the nuns, to see Pansy. 'I've come to say goodbye,' she said. 'I'm going to England.'

Pansy's white little face turned red. 'To England! When will you come back?'

'I don't know, Pansy. My cousin is very sick. I wish to see him.'

'Ah yes, of course you must go. And will papa go?'

'No,' said Isabel.

The girl said nothing for a time, then she looked at Isabel and said, 'You're not happy, Mrs Osmond. Perhaps you won't come back?'

'Perhaps not. I can't tell.'

'Don't leave me here,' said Pansy softly.

Isabel's heart went faster. 'Will you come away with me now?'

'Did papa say that?'

'No, it's my idea.'

'Then I must wait here,' said Pansy, sadly. 'But when you're not here I am a little afraid.'

'What are you afraid of?'

'Don't leave me here,' said Pansy softly.

'Of papa – a little. And of Madame Merle. She was here tonight. I don't like her.'

'You must never say that,' said Isabel.

They walked together to the top of the stairs. 'Goodbye, my child,' said Isabel, as she started to go down.

'You'll come back?' called Pansy, in a voice that Isabel could never forget.

'Yes – I'll come back.'

Madame Merle was waiting for Isabel downstairs. 'I know Pansy does not like me,' she explained, 'but I came to say goodbye.'

Isabel said nothing.

'You're very unhappy, I know,' said Madame Merle. 'But I am more so. I am going to live in America. And you? To England? Ah, poor Ralph! Did you know it was his idea to give you a fortune?'

Chapter 15   Saying Goodbye

On the long train journey Isabel felt dead. At Gardencourt, waiting for her aunt to welcome her, she thought of that wet afternoon in America when they first met. 'Caspar Goodwood came to see me the same day,' she remembered. 'Was I right not to marry him?'

Isabel sat next to Ralph's bed, without hope. He knew her, but could not speak for three days. At last he said, 'Ah, Isabel, with me it's finished. I am glad you came. And what about you?'

Suddenly Isabel put her head in her hands and started to cry. Ralph lay silent, listening to her.

'What have you done for me, Ralph?' she cried. 'I never knew. I never thanked you. Is it true – is it true?'

'Your fortune?' he said. 'Yes, it's true. It was my idea, but it was a mistake.'

'Osmond married me for the money,' said Isabel. She wanted to speak honestly now.

'And now you are unhappy. Will you go back to him?'

'I don't know – I can't tell. I just want to stay here.'

'Please stay here,' said Ralph. 'Be happy. And keep me in your heart. Remember that I've always loved you.'

'Oh, my brother,' she cried.

The next morning Ralph was dead.

♦

Three days later, many important people came to the church near Gardencourt. Isabel knew only Lord Warburton and one tall American. Why was he there? They did not speak.

Isabel stayed at Gardencourt, with no thoughts for the future. Her aunt was busy. Lord Warburton came to tell them he planned to marry an English girl, and Isabel was glad.

One evening, while she was sitting in the garden, she saw a tall shadow. 'Don't be afraid,' said Caspar Goodwood, quickly. 'I came from London by train today. I want to help you. I visited your cousin before he died. He told me about you – I know you are unhappy. He asked me to look after you. And I can, Isabel. The world is very big. We'll never be afraid together. Be mine, as I am yours.'

Isabel had a sudden feeling of danger. 'Please go away,' she said. She was crying now.

'Ah, don't say that. Don't kill me!' said Caspar, and he kissed her hard. To Isabel the kiss was white-hot. It seemed to be something to rest on. Slowly she moved from darkness to light. Slowly she knew where to go. There was a very straight road.

When Caspar Goodwood came to Gardencourt again two days later, they told him. 'Mrs Osmond has gone to London.

'Ah, don't say that. Don't kill me!' said Caspar.

She is with Miss Stackpole.' He knew Henrietta was back in Europe again, and he went straight to the house where she was staying. Henrietta answered the door.

'Oh, good morning,' he said. 'I was hoping to find Mrs Osmond.'

Henrietta looked at him. 'She was here yesterday, and spent the night,' she said. 'But this morning she started for Rome.'

Caspar Goodwood could not move.

Henrietta touched his arm. 'Mr Goodwood,' she said kindly, 'just you wait.' But he thought she was wrong to give him hope.

ACTIVITIES

Chapters 1–5

Before you read

1 What kind of story do you think this will be? A story about love?
   or crime? or adventure? Say why. The pictures in the book will
   help you.

2 All these words come in this part of the story. Find their meanings
   in your dictionary. Then put them in the correct places in the
   sentences below.
   admire care for certainly class independent thoughts wish
   After they met, his ..... soon turned to marriage, because he .....
   her very much. He belonged to a higher ..... than she did but
   she knew that he ..... her. She ..... didn't want to get married
   immediately: her real ..... was to be ..... for a time.

3 One of the people in the story is a *lord*. This means that he is:
   a a soldier and high officer
   b a man with a title
   c a man who owns a lot of land

After you read

4 Change these sentences to make them true.
   a After her father died, Isabel had a lot of money.
   b She decided to leave America with her sisters.
   c First she went to her uncle's house in Italy.
   d She made friends with her English cousin Ralph.

5 In Chapter 5, Ralph says: 'I think I will dislike her.'
   a Who is he talking about?
   b What did he think of her when they met?

6 Answer these questions:
   a Who writes to Isabel?
   b What does he ask for in the letter?

Chapters 6–10

Before you read

7 What does *fortune* mean:
   a bad weather
   b a large amount of money
   c a kind of cake

8 In Chapter 9, Henrietta speaks of 'hope for the future'. What word means the opposite of *future*?

9 On which page can you find a picture of two *nuns*?

10 Do you think that Isabel will stay in Europe or return to the United States? Why? Talk about this with other students.

After you read

11 Answer these questions:
   a At Gardencourt, what does Lord Warburton ask Isabel?
   b How does Isabel reply?
   c Caspar says: 'I don't want to lose you.' What answer does Isabel give?

12 In Chapter 7, Isabel says: 'My poor Ralph!' Why?

13 In Florence:
   a Where did Isabel stay?
   b Who helped Gilbert Osmond to meet her?
   c What did Osmond know about Isabel?

14 In Rome:
   a Who was Isabel surprised to meet again?
   b What did Osmond ask Isabel?

Chapters 11–15

Before you read

15 Do you think that the story will end happily or unhappily for Isabel? Say why.

After you read

16 Who says these things and what do they mean?

   a 'I will not trouble you again.'

   b 'Your fortune is enough for Pansy but I'm afraid it isn't large enough for her father.'

   c 'I'm sure you will be happy – you've got a very good friend.'

17 Four men love Isabel in different ways: Caspar Goodwood, Lord Warburton, Ralph Touchett and Gilbert Osmond. Talk about these men. In what ways is their love for Isabel different? Why was Osmond the wrong one to marry?

18 At the end of the story Isabel leaves for Rome because of a promise she made.

   a Who did she make the promise to?

   b What was the promise?

Writing

19 Describe a day which Isabel spends with her friends visiting famous places in London or in Rome.

20 You are Madame Merle. Write a letter to Pansy in which you tell her that you are her real mother.

21 Write a different ending to the story in which both Isabel and Pansy are truly happy.

22 Write a note about this book to a friend. Say if you think they will like it or dislike it and give your reasons.

The Secret Agent

JOSEPH CONRAD

Level 3

Retold by Robin Waterfield
Series Editors: Andy Hopkins and Jocelyn Potter

Contents

Introduction

'When I say we want action,' Mr Vladimir went on, 'I don't mean that people have to die. We just want to frighten people. Buildings are enough. But which buildings? That's the question. What do you think, Mr Verloc?'

Mr Verloc didn't know. He said nothing …

Mr Verloc is a fat man who owns a bookshop in London. He is happily married to a pretty young woman called Winnie. Winnie's brother, Stevie, lives with them. Stevie is a good-looking boy but he has a problem. There is something wrong with his head and he can't remember things. So Mr Verloc and Winnie have to look after him.

Mr Verloc is very lazy. He just wants to be comfortable and to look after his shop. But he is also an anarchist. He belongs to a group of anarchists who have meetings in his house. They all want to see a revolution in Britain, but Mr Verloc doesn't really want to do very much about it. He wants a revolution just to happen.

Mr Vladimir works in the Russian Embassy. He orders Mr Verloc to bomb an important scientific building in London. This is very difficult for Mr Verloc. Will he do the job? *Can* he do the job? And what happens when the plan all goes terribly wrong?

The Secret Agent (1907) takes place in London in the late 1880s. At this time in Europe and Russia the political movement called anarchism, which disagreed with all forms of government, was becoming popular. Conrad's story is very exciting, with surprises on every page. But it is far more than just an adventure story. It is also a study of the badness that can lie at the heart of man.

Joseph Conrad was very unusual. He was an adventurer as well as a great writer. He was born Joseph Teodor Konrad Korzeniowski in 1857 in an area of Poland which is now part of the Ukraine. His parents were both Polish and were very interested in politics. They were against the Russians who were strong in this part of Poland, and in the end the family had to leave their home. Both his parents were dead by the time Conrad was eleven years old. He was then looked after by his uncle.

Conrad joined a French ship at the age of seventeen and spent the next twenty years at sea. He sailed around much of the world and had many adventures. A lot of the stories which he wrote later were about the sea. The year 1878 was a very important one in Conrad's life. He tried to kill himself, and later began to work on English ships. In 1886 he became British.

In 1894 Conrad decided to stop being a sailor and spend all his time writing. He married Jessie George in 1895 and they had two sons. In the same year his book, *Almayer's Folly*, came out. This was the first of many books by Conrad which takes place at sea.

Although many important British writers thought Conrad's writing was great, he was not really successful until 1913 with his book *Chance*. Conrad died in 1924, at the age of sixty-seven. By the time of his death, he was both rich and successful as a writer.

Conrad is one of the greatest writers in English literature. He was much more than just a writer of adventure stories, and is seen as one of the most important writers in the 'Modernist' movement. Other writers who belonged to this movement were the Irish writer, James Joyce, and the American poet, T. S. Eliot. These writers understood that the way of life in one country is not better or worse than the way of life in another. Conrad travelled widely and many of his stories are about people's lives in different parts of the world.

Conrad's novels are mainly about the badness in people. People love others and are then hurt by them, or they hurt themselves. In *The Secret Agent*, Winnie loves Verloc, her husband, and is badly hurt by him. Almost none of the people in *The Secret Agent* are good people. The anarchists are either lazy or cold-blooded. The detectives are just interested in money and getting information. Only Winnie and Stevie are good, but at the end of the story Winnie also becomes bad. All the people in the story do things that neither they nor the reader think they will do. Conrad's own family was political and *The Secret Agent* is the world's first political story, with spies, dishonest policemen, bombs and murder. The story shows Conrad's feelings of hatred towards Russians, who took over Poland, his country, and killed his parents.

Conrad wrote many books. The most famous ones *are Lord Jim, Nostromo, Heart of Darkness* and *The Secret Agent*. Many people think that this book is one of the best books that anyone has ever written in the English language. *The Secret Agent* is also a film, with Bob Hoskins, Gerard Depardieu, and Patricia Arquette.

Chapter 1   The Lazy Shopkeeper

Mr Verloc went out in the morning, leaving his wife's brother to look after the shop and his wife to look after her brother. This was all right, because very few customers came into the shop before the evenings.

The shop was small, and so was the house. They lived in a back room behind the shop, and in the bedrooms upstairs. The house was dirty, in a poor part of London. The shop was like a square box. In the daytime the door stayed closed; in the evenings it was open a little.

The shop window showed pictures of dancing-girls without many clothes on. There were also mysterious boxes and packets, some books and some newspapers. The books were not the sort that anyone showed to respectable people. No one seemed interested in the newspapers, which were yellow with age. Mr Verloc's anarchist friends wrote them.

The shop's customers were either very young men, who waited by the window for a time before suddenly going in, or older men with dirty clothes. They pushed their hands into the pockets of their coats and pulled their hats low over their faces before going into the shop. Customers went into the shop quickly, but they could not escape the old bell. As soon as anyone came into the shop, the bell made a loud sound.

At the sound of the bell Mr Verloc left the back room and came into the shop. He was a fat man, with heavy eyes. When you saw him, you thought that he slept in his clothes. In most businesses, people need to wear nice clothes and to look nice. But in Mr Verloc's business it didn't matter. His customers paid the high prices that Mr Verloc asked, without worrying about the clothes of the shopkeeper.

Sometimes Mrs Verloc came into the shop at the sound of the bell.
Winnie Verloc was a young, pretty woman.

Sometimes Mrs Verloc came into the shop at the sound of the bell. Winnie Verloc was a young, pretty woman. When she came into the shop, young customers couldn't meet her eyes. They bought something useless, like a pencil. They paid too much for the pencil, but as soon as they were out of the shop, they threw it away angrily.

Customers were not the only people to push through the dirty door. In the evenings Mr Verloc sometimes had visitors. They said hello to Mrs Verloc and walked past her into the back room.

Mr Verloc was a lazy man who liked his life to be comfortable. And his life *was* comfortable. He had some money. His wife looked after him, and she seemed happy. She seemed to admire him, and what more can a respectable man want?

When Winnie was younger, Winnie's mother had a small hotel. Some men stayed in the hotel for months or years, and others stayed just for a few nights while they had business in London. Winnie helped her mother to look after the hotel. The men all liked her. She was pretty, and she had beautiful, thick black hair. She was also quiet, and didn't talk much, and the men liked that too. Mr Verloc stayed at the hotel when he was in London. He seemed respectable, and he always had money.

When Mr Verloc and Winnie got married, they decided to leave the hotel. Winnie's mother sold it, and Mr Verloc and his new wife took some furniture from it for their new house. And along with the furniture went Stevie. Winnie's mother was glad that she didn't have to worry about Stevie. Mr Verloc had money; Mr Verloc could look after Stevie. And Winnie always loved Stevie.

Stevie was a problem. He was a good-looking boy, but weak. He could read and write, but was not much help in the hotel. There was something wrong with his head. He could not remember things. Outside, he could not find his way home, and could not remember his address. Sudden questions and noises worried him a lot. His sentences were never good, but when he was worried they were worse. He got angry easily, and then he could speak only one or two words.

So Stevie came with the furniture to Mr Verloc's new house, with the shop in front. And there he sat all day, making circles on pieces of paper, while Winnie looked at him from time to time, in the way that a mother looks at her child.

Chapter 2   A Dangerous Plan

Mr Verloc left the house at 10.30 in the morning. It was unusually early for him. The sun shone, and he walked past Hyde Park where men and women were riding horses, and people were walking. He wore his blue coat, his boots were black and shiny, and his face seemed fresh and clean. His heavy eyes were more awake than usual. Carriages drove past on the roads, pulled by horses, with women's faces at the windows.

Mr Verloc could see that the people in the carriages and in the park were rich. The rich were weak and they had to guard themselves and their money against the poor. So the rich were afraid of the poor, and the poor hated the rich. Mr Verloc was an anarchist, and he wanted to see a revolution in Britain. He did not want to *do* very much, because he was lazy, but he wanted a revolution just to happen. So he was happy that the rich and the poor were enemies.

Mr Verloc arrived in Chesham Square and knocked on the door of a large house. It was the Embassy of a foreign country. A servant opened the door and Mr Verloc walked inside. He pulled a letter from his pocket and showed it to the servant, who looked at it and then took Mr Verloc to a room. Mr Verloc waited in the room for a few minutes, and then he heard a door open behind him.

Mr Verloc knocked on the door of a large house.
It was the Embassy of a foreign country.

At first, when he turned, he saw only black clothes, the top of a head, and some papers. The man was reading the papers as he walked into the room. He went over to the table and put the papers down on it. Then he put on some glasses and turned to look at Mr Verloc.

'My name is Vladimir,' the man said, and he picked up the papers again. 'We have here some of your reports.'

Mr Verloc waited. What was this man going to say?

'We're not happy about the police in this country,' Mr Vladimir continued. He seemed tired.

For the first time since he left his home that morning, Mr Verloc opened his lips. 'Every country has its police,' he said. But the Embassy man just continued to look at him, so Mr Verloc went on: 'You know that I cannot do anything about the police here.'

'We want to see something happen,' Mr Vladimir said. 'Something big. You can do that, can't you?'

Mr Verloc didn't answer. 'The police here are too soft,' Mr Vladimir said. He went and sat down behind a desk. 'We want them to be harder. Then ordinary people will be afraid of them . . . and then ordinary people will want a change, a revolution perhaps. Do you see? People here do not hate the police enough.'

'Of course,' said Mr Verloc, who was not unintelligent. 'If you read my reports, you will see that the ordinary people of this country are already unhappy. Things are getting quite dangerous here.'

'I have read your reports,' said Mr Vladimir. 'I cannot understand why you wrote them. They are useless. We already *know* things are dangerous. Why do you think we use you and pay you money? We do not pay you to tell us what we already know, but to make things worse than they are. We do not want reports; we want to see something real happen.'

'I'll do my best,' Mr Verloc started to say, but he stopped because the other man was just looking hard at him.

'You're very fat,' the other man said rudely. He spoke in French.

'What did you say?' Mr Verloc asked.

Respectable people in London knew Mr Vladimir well, and liked him. He was amusing and told stories well. But Mr Verloc could see no amusement in his face. Mr Vladimir sat back in his chair and looked hard at Mr Verloc without moving his eyes.

'You understand French, don't you?' he said.

Mr Verloc explained that he was half French and lived there for a long time. He stood in the middle of the room holding his hat in one hand and feeling helpless. But then Mr Vladimir changed to English for the rest of the conversation.

'Ah, yes, of course,' he said. 'You were in prison there, weren't you? For five years? You sold us some secrets. How did they catch you?'

'A woman ...' began Mr Verloc. 'She took my money, and told the police.'

'That wasn't very clever,' Mr Vladimir said. 'So what do you want?'

'I don't have anything to say,' said Mr Verloc. 'I got a letter. You wanted to see me.'

'How can you call yourself an anarchist?' Mr Vladimir said. 'You're too fat. You're not poor and hungry. I think you're lazy. And how long have we paid you from the Embassy here? How long have you worked for us in this country?'

'For eleven years,' said Mr Verloc. 'Since Baron Stott-Wartenheim was here. He used me several times. I came to London at first because he asked me to.'

'Ah, yes, the Baron,' said Mr Vladimir. 'Yes ... he got a lot of soft, lazy people to work for us. But things must change. I asked you to come here to tell you this: you have to work for your money now. I see that you understand me. We don't want reports; we want action.'

'But only three months ago, when the Duke Romuald was

visiting Paris, I warned the Baron that some people wanted to try to kill the Duke. Don't you remember?'

'The French police didn't need your warning,' said Mr Vladimir. 'And now I repeat: we don't want words, we must have action. We want the British to wake up. Why do you anarchists just write stupid newspapers which nobody reads? You're all lazy. What can I do with you?'

'Why did you ask me to come here to the Embassy at eleven in the morning?' asked Mr Verloc, a little angry. He was better with words than with actions; he was unhappy that this young man was trying to get him to do something. 'It's dangerous for me to come here in the morning. If someone sees me, I'll stop being useful to you.'

'That's your problem,' said Mr Vladimir. 'When you stop being useful, we stop paying you.'

Mr Verloc's legs felt weak and he wanted suddenly to sit down.

'When I say that we want action,' Mr Vladimir went on, 'I don't mean that people have to die. We just want to frighten people. Buildings are enough. But which buildings? That's the question. What do you think, Mr Verloc?'

Mr Verloc didn't know. He said nothing. He was frightened of traps.

'I'll tell you,' Mr Vladimir said. 'Today people love and admire science. They thank science for their comfortable lives. So if we want to frighten them, we must attack a science building. The newspapers won't be able to use all their old, tired words to talk about *that*. Usually when a bomb attack happens, on a king, perhaps, or a theatre, people just say, "Oh, some poor people did that," and then they forget about it. But what about a bomb attack which people can't explain? *Then* they'll wake up. And it must be a famous building. I'll tell you the building that I'm thinking about, if you like. Can you guess?'

Mr Verloc just stood there, saying nothing. Mr Vladimir rested his arms on his desk, looked up at Mr Verloc and went on: 'The Greenwich Observatory!* You see? Everyone in the world, rich and poor, has heard of the Greenwich Observatory. It's perfect!'

Mr Vladimir looked very pleased with himself. 'It won't be easy,' was all that Mr Verloc could say.

'What's the problem?' asked Mr Vladimir. 'You have a whole group of anarchists, don't you? Yundt is here in London – I've seen him. And there's Michaelis: he's out of prison now. Do you know where he is? If you don't, I can tell you. You mustn't think you're the only person that we pay.'

'It will cost money,' Mr Verloc said.

'Don't worry,' said Mr Vladimir. 'We'll still pay you every month – but first we must see some action. And if nothing happens soon, we'll stop paying you anything. What's your job – I mean, when you're not working for us?'

'I keep a shop,' answered Mr Verloc.

'A shop! What sort of shop?'

'Oh, newspapers and things. My wife . . .'

'Your wife? You're married? And you call yourself an anarchist!'

'Well, my wife isn't an anarchist. And it's none of your business.'

'Oh, yes, it is,' said Mr Vladimir. 'I'm not sure any more that you're the man for the job.' He was silent for a short time, thinking. Then he said, 'You can go now. You can have a month. There must be a bomb by then. Is that clear? If nothing happens, you'll stop working for us.'

He returned to the work on his desk, and Mr Verloc left the room. The same servant showed him out of the Embassy.

Mr Verloc walked back home without noticing anything. He went in and sat down at the back of the shop. No one came in to say anything to him. Stevie was cleaning the house upstairs. Mrs

* The Greenwich Observatory is a famous building where scientists study the stars.

111

Verloc looked through the door when she heard the shop bell, but then returned to the kitchen when she saw that it was her husband.

An hour later she called towards the shop: 'Adolf!' Mr Verloc was still sitting in the same place. He got up heavily and came to dinner. People in this house didn't talk much, but Mr Verloc was strangely quiet at dinner. They could see that he was thinking hard. Winnie sat silent herself, watching Stevie. She did not want him suddenly to start talking. Every day she told him to be quiet and not to worry Mr Verloc.

When Stevie was very young, his mother and sister told him not to worry his father. After his father died, they told him not to worry the men who stayed at the hotel. And now they told him not to worry Mr Verloc. So Stevie admired Mr Verloc. He thought that Mr Verloc was an important man.

Mr Verloc did not notice Stevie much. Once Winnie's mother asked Winnie, 'Do you think that Mr Verloc is tired of having Stevie at your house?' And Winnie answered, 'He'll have to get tired of me first.'

'It was very sensible of you to marry Mr Verloc,' her mother said, but then stopped. She didn't understand. Why did Winnie marry an older man? There was that young man, the son of a butcher, but Winnie saw him only a few times. Then Mr Verloc started to stay at the hotel, and now . . . Well, Winnie was very sensible.

Chapter 3   Talk, Talk, Talk

There was a meeting of the anarchist group in the back room behind Mr Verloc's shop. Michaelis was speaking. 'Things do not change because thinkers want them to change; things change because of the men with tools, because of the workers. What will happen next? You do not need to think about it. It's useless to think about it, because your thinking won't change anything. Do you understand?'

When Michaelis went into prison, he was thin. After fifteen years in prison, he came out fat. People said that a rich old woman was looking after Michaelis, by giving him money and sending him to doctors. She wanted to see him healthy again.

'You see,' he went on, 'prison gave me plenty of time to think about things.'

He was sitting on one side of the fire. In a chair on the other side – the chair in which Winnie usually sat – was Karl Yundt. He opened his mouth to laugh at Michaelis's words, and showed that there were no teeth in his mouth. He was old and had no hair on the top of his head, but a thin white beard below. He looked at the world with hard black eyes. Now he said, 'I always wanted to see a few men who were strong enough to kill others without pity. The world needs a group like this. That is the way for things to change for the better, if you ask me. But I could never find these men. There was only me.'

Mr Verloc, sitting on the sofa across the room, smiled his agreement.

'But you, Michaelis,' Yundt finished, 'you only want things to get worse.'

'That's not true!' said Michaelis. 'It's true that I see war between the rich and the poor, but in the end the workers will win and a new golden time will begin for man. In prison I *had* to think like this. It was either that or killing myself!'

The fourth person in the room, listening to this conversation, was Alexander Ossipon – they called him 'the Doctor'. For some years he was a student, because he wanted to be a doctor, but he left the university. Ossipon wrote most of the cheap newspapers which the anarchists tried to sell. Now he sat warming his feet in front of the fire. He had yellow hair and a strong, thick body. He wore a shirt and a tie under his coat, and his head rested on the back of the chair. From time to time he lifted a cigarette to his lips and blew smoke towards the ceiling.

Michaelis continued to talk. He talked to himself, really. Were the others listening? It didn't matter to him. He was better at talking to himself than at talking to others, because of his time in prison. And so he talked on and on ... but then a laugh from Ossipon cut his voice off. Michaelis looked surprised, and then he closed his eyes. The only sound in the room was the noise of the gas lights. With the fire and the lights, the room was starting to be very hot. Mr Verloc got up and opened the door into the kitchen. Now the men in the room could see Stevie, who was sitting at the kitchen table, making circles on pieces of paper. He did not turn or move his head to look at them; he just continued with his work.

Ossipon got up and went into the kitchen. He looked over Stevie's shoulder at the circles on the paper. When he came back to the others, he said, 'Of course, he's weak in the head. People like him are always making circles on paper, or something like that. The scientists' books are full of examples. If you read the books of Lombroso ...'

Mr Verloc's face went a little red. When he heard the word 'scientist' these days, he always thought of Mr Vladimir. He could almost see him in the room, standing in front of him with his clean-shaven face and his hard smile. But he said nothing.

'Lombroso is stupid,' said Karl Yundt.

'What do you mean?' asked Ossipon.

'Because when he wants to understand criminals, he looks in prisons. But the real criminals are not in prisons. The real criminals are the others, who put people in prisons. And it's stupid to think that you can look at people's teeth and ears and decide about them. If you want to know a prisoner ... well, the police burn numbers into prisoners' skin.'

Michaelis talked to himself, really. Were the others listening?
It didn't matter to him.

Michaelis smiled. Ossipon began to speak. 'You don't understand ...' he said, but stopped, frightened by the look in Yundt's eyes.

Stevie got up from his chair just before Yundt began to speak. He wanted to go to bed, but when he was walking past the door, he heard Yundt talk of the police and burning. Stevie knew that hot metal on skin hurts. He stood still with his eyes wide open; his pieces of paper fell out of his hands and on to the floor. His mouth dropped open.

For a few minutes, after Yundt's angry words, no one spoke. Then Michaelis began again. He talked of the end of war, of the good times that were coming for all men.

'If you're right, Michaelis,' Ossipon said, 'we don't have to do anything. The good times will just come. But you're wrong. We can't be sure. There's only one important thing: the workers must feel angry. Then change will come, but it will not just come without action. This is science. Don't you agree, Verloc?'

But Verloc had nothing to say. He heard the word 'science' again and was quiet.

'Why are we thinking about tomorrow?' said Yundt. 'What about today? I think today the rich are eating the bodies of the poor and drinking their blood.'

At these frightening words, Stevie sat down hard on the floor. Before long the three anarchists left Mr Verloc and went home. Mr Verloc closed the door behind them with a crash. He was not pleased with his friends. He had a bomb to think about, and he could see that his friends were useless. They were lazy – Michaelis with his rich old woman, Ossipon with his girlfriends, Yundt with the woman who looked after him. And they did not know Vladimir. He was dangerous.

He turned off the gas lights and began to go to bed. Then he saw Stevie, who was in the kitchen, walking round the table and waving his hands. 'What's the boy doing there?' Mr Verloc asked himself. He didn't ask the boy because he spoke very little to him. In the morning, he said, 'Give me my boots,' and that was an order, not a question. So what could he say to the boy now? He had no idea.

He went upstairs and woke his wife. She went downstairs to look after Stevie, while Mr Verloc undressed and got ready for bed. When she came back into the room, he was sitting on the bed, looking at the floor.

'What are you doing there?' she asked.

'I don't feel very well,' he said. 'I have a headache.'

'Well, come to bed,' Winnie said. 'It's cold.'

He lay down in bed and looked up at the ceiling.

'Not many customers in the shop today,' said Winnie.

'No. Did you turn off the gas downstairs?'

'Yes, I did. That poor boy is very excited tonight. I think he heard some of your conversation. It's not good for him. He feels things very quickly and easily. If he hears bad things, he gets angry and excited.' She wanted her husband to know that Stevie was not bad, but just excited. She had to look after Stevie – and this meant that her husband must not think badly of the boy.

'He hears too much,' she went on. 'He was talking about burning skin and blood and things. He was saying, "Bad! Bad! Bad world for poor people!" It's not right. What were you talking about downstairs?'

'Ask Karl Yundt,' said Mr Verloc angrily.

'That man,' she said. 'I don't like him. Michaelis is all right.'

'I've had this headache for a few days now,' Mr Verloc said.

'Perhaps it was wrong to send Stevie to school,' Winnie said. 'He reads the newspapers from the shop, and gets angry at them too. There was a story the other day about a German soldier pulling off someone's ear. I couldn't do anything with Stevie that afternoon.'

Mr Verloc said nothing.

'Are you comfortable now, my dear?' she asked. 'Shall I turn off the light?'

Mr Verloc was sure that there was no sleep waiting for him that night. 'Yes,' he said. 'Turn off the light.'

Chapter 4   A Terrible Accident

Ossipon walked into the pub. There were about thirty tables against the walls. He bought himself a beer and looked for a place to sit. He saw a man at one of the tables, and looked surprised. He went over to the table and spoke to the man.

'You'll be able to help me to understand this business,' he said.

The little man with glasses waited for the noise in the pub to die down. Then he said, 'If I do know something, why do you think I'll tell you?' When he stopped talking he picked up the glass of beer from the table in front of him and had a long drink. Ossipon looked at the little man. He was small and weak, but he seemed so sure of himself. He spoke in short sentences, but was perfectly happy not to say anything sometimes.

Ossipon said, 'Have you been out much today?'

'No. I stayed in bed all the morning,' answered the other. 'Why?'

Ossipon *did* want to know something, but in front of this little man, the big Ossipon always felt small, so he said, 'Oh, nothing.' But then he tried another question: 'Did you walk down here?'

'No, I took a bus.' The little man lived in north London, in a room in a small house. His room was ordinary, but it had a very large cupboard. When the servant came to clean his room, the little man did not leave the room, but carefully watched the cleaner. When he left the house, he always locked his room and took his key with him.

'Have you been here long?' Ossipon asked.

'An hour or more,' answered the other.

'An hour,' said Ossipon. 'Then perhaps you haven't heard the news. I heard it only just now, in the street.'

The little man shook his head, but didn't seem to want to know the news. Ossipon said, 'I didn't know that you were in here. I just came in here for a drink.'

'Oh, I come here sometimes,' the other man said.

'It's strange that you, of all people, haven't heard the news,' Ossipon continued. 'You of all people.'

But still the little man said nothing. 'Do you give your explosives to anyone who asks you for them?' asked Ossipon.

'Yes, I never say no, as long as I have some to give,' answered the little man.

'Do you think you're right to do that?'

'Yes, I'm sure of it. Why not?'

'And if a detective asks you for some?'

'Hah! They don't come near me,' said the little man. 'They're too afraid. It's dangerous.'

'Why?'

'Because they know very well that I always have some explosives on me.' He touched the pocket of his coat lightly. 'It's in a thick bottle,' he said.

'Yes, people have told me,' Ossipon said. 'But if six of them jump on you and hold you, you won't be able to do anything.'

'You're wrong. I never walk outside after dark, and I always walk with my right hand in my pocket. I hold a rubber ball lightly in my hand. I only have to push this ball and twenty seconds later . . .'

'You have to wait twenty seconds!' said Ossipon. 'That's terrible!'

'It doesn't matter. I have the explosives, but that's not important. I'm brave enough to push the ball – that's the

'I have to tell you that a bomb killed a man in Greenwich Park
this morning.'

important thing. And the police know it, so they stay away from me. I'm the only true anarchist, you know. I never play. I work fourteen hours a day, and go hungry sometimes. Explosives cost money, so sometimes I don't have money for food. I see you're looking at my drink. Yes, I've had two beers already, and after this I'll have another one. Why not? I'm having a holiday.'

'I'm afraid you won't be happy after you've heard me,' said Ossipon. 'I have to tell you that a bomb killed a man in Greenwich Park this morning.'

'How do you know?'

'It's in the newspapers. I bought a paper and ran in here to read it. Then I saw you. I've got it in my pocket now.'

He pulled out the newspaper. 'Ah, here it is. Bomb in Greenwich Park, at half past eleven this morning. A foggy morning. Large hole in the ground under a tree. Pieces of a man's body all over the place, and leaves and bits of tree. They think the man was trying to bomb the Observatory.'

He gave the newspaper to the other man, who read it and put it down on the table. He didn't say anything.

'What have you done?' Ossipon asked. 'You didn't plan this, did you? Tell me, who did you give the explosives to?'

'All right, I'll tell you. Verloc.'

'Verloc! Impossible!'

'No, true, I'm afraid. He was an important man in your group, wasn't he?'

'More useful than important. And the police never seemed to notice him. That was good. He was married, you know. What will that woman do now?' He stopped to think.

The little man waited. He was called 'the Scientist' by his friends. No one knew his real name.

'Did Verloc tell you anything?' Ossipon asked at last. 'Why did he want the explosives?'

'He said they were for a building. The bomb was safe. "Put it

121

against the building," I told him, "and then run away. In twenty minutes . . . boom!"'

'What went wrong, do you think?'

'I don't know. Perhaps he dropped it.'

'It's a bad time for this,' Ossipon said. 'Yundt is ill in bed: he's probably dying. Michaelis is out of town somewhere, writing a book. I'm the only one left now. I want the police to know that Verloc did this without us, without the help of the group. But how can I tell them?'

The Scientist was paying a waiter and getting ready to leave. Ossipon continued to think out loud. 'No, of course, the police don't know anything. Verloc is in small pieces. The police have no idea. Did anyone see him? Can anyone say, "It was Mr Verloc?" I don't think so. It was foggy. Good, good. Perhaps everything will be all right for the rest of us. Perhaps I'll go to the shop. I don't think that it's a trap.'

'Yes,' said the Scientist, the perfect anarchist, 'why don't you do that? Go to the woman.'

Chapter 5   A Bad Day for Heat

Detective Inspector Heat was having a bad day. First he missed breakfast. Then there was that bomb. He had to look at the bits of body. He felt sick. The body lay on a table in the Greenwich Park police station. While he was looking at the body, he asked the Park policeman, 'Did anyone see anything?'

'Yes, an old woman saw two men. They came out of the railway station and walked towards the park. One was a big man. The other was a young man with fair hair. And you can see that this man here' – he pointed to the bits on the table – 'had fair hair. The old woman said that he was carrying some kind of tin in his hand, and was walking a little behind the big man.'

'Do you know this old woman?'

'Yes, she's honest.'

'What about the big man?'

'She couldn't say. There was a lot of fog. She only really noticed the younger man.'

'What do you think happened?'

'I think that he fell over a stone in the park.'

'Yes,' said Detective Inspector Heat, 'that seems possible.' He saw on the table a piece of coat, and he picked it up. There was some writing on it. He took it over to the window for a better look. Now he could read the writing – and his face showed great surprise. He pushed the piece of coat into his pocket and left the police station.

He went back to London by train, thinking deeply. This piece of coat was very important. 'But what do I tell my boss, the Assistant Commissioner of Police?' he thought. 'Is it better to catch this bomber or not? I really don't know. Why did I find this piece of coat? It was so easy; it was like a present to me. But what do I do with this present, this information?'

Heat didn't like his work these days. He didn't like making reports to his bosses. It was an interesting problem. 'If I don't tell him all that I know,' he thought, 'he'll never know.'

He went to the Assistant Commissioner's office to make a report. The Assistant Commissioner was working at his desk. He looked up at Heat. 'What news from Greenwich?' he asked.

Detective Inspector Heat gave a clear report. He watched the sunlight on the Assistant Commissioner's desk and black hair. The Assistant Commissioner rested his head in his hands. When Heat finished, he waited. He was thinking, 'Do I tell him the rest?' But the Assistant Commissioner thought that he was waiting for him to speak.

'So you think that there were two men?' he said.

'Yes,' said Heat. 'The other man left the park unseen in the fog. He took the young man to the park and left him there to do the job. He was probably waiting back at the railway station when he heard the bomb. He knew it was too soon for the bomb, so he ran away.'

'Which train were the two men on?' said the Assistant Commissioner.

'I asked at the railway station. They came from Kent.* The station guard remembers them. "The big man was carrying a shiny tin," he said, "and then he gave it to the young man." The young man followed the big man out of the station.'

'Who were these men?' the Assistant Commissioner went on. 'You told me this morning that they weren't from London. You didn't think that our London anarchists were bombers. So we have two foreign anarchists coming from Kent. That's very strange.'

'Perhaps it's not so strange, Assistant Commissioner. Michaelis is living near the station which they came from.'

Chapter 6   32 Brett Street

The important woman who looked after Michaelis and gave him money was a friend of the Assistant Commissioner's wife. Michaelis was in prison for a long time because he was an anarchist, not because he was a terrible criminal. When he was very young some people he knew wanted to save some men from prison. They asked Michaelis to help. He thought that it was an adventure, so he agreed to help. But the other men shot and killed one of the prison guards. The police caught Michaelis and threw him in prison. When he came out, the important woman

---

* Part of south-east England, near London.

felt sorry for him. 'He's not dangerous,' she said, and the Assistant Commissioner agreed.

When Detective Inspector Heat spoke Michaelis's name, the Assistant Commissioner thought, 'What do I do now?' He didn't want to hurt the important woman, and he honestly didn't think that Michaelis was a dangerous bomber. The important woman was kind to him and to his wife – *that* was important to him, so he didn't want Michaelis to get into trouble. 'Prison will kill Michaelis; he won't come out alive.'

'Do you think Michaelis helped the bombers?' he asked Heat.

'Two bombers come from that part of Kent,' answered Heat. 'Yes, I think we must question Michaelis.'

The Assistant Commissioner was worried. When he was younger, he was an adventurous policeman and detective. Now he was sitting behind a desk, and men like Heat could change everything for him, while he could do nothing. But perhaps he could. A plan was beginning to come to him.

'If Michaelis is so important,' he said, 'why didn't you speak of him immediately? You gave your report. You were in my office for twenty minutes before speaking his name. I think that you were thinking of another person at first. If I'm right, tell me: who is this other person?'

Detective Inspector Heat was surprised. The Assistant Commissioner was very clever. 'If I don't tell him about that piece of coat now,' he thought, 'I'll be in big trouble.'

'Yes,' he said, 'I was coming to that part of my report.'

'What have you got?' asked the Assistant Commissioner.

'I have an address,' answered the Detective Inspector, pulling the piece of coat out of his pocket. 'This belongs to the bomber: he was wearing it when he died. Look at this.'

The Assistant Commissioner took the burned piece of coat. He could see on it a number and two words: 32 Brett Street. He was surprised.

'Why did the bomber have his address on his coat?' he asked. 'Parents do that for their children sometimes, but this man was no child. But what is 32 Brett Street, Detective Inspector. Do you know?'

'It's a shop,' said the Detective Inspector.

The Assistant Commissioner waited, but Heat said nothing more. The Assistant Commissioner had to question him. At last he heard Mr Verloc's name. He looked up at the Detective Inspector.

'And you say that we don't have this man's name on paper here in this office?'

'That's right. It was enough for me to know him, and to use him when I wanted to. A friend of mine in the French police told me he was an Embassy spy. When Baron Stott-Wartenheim was at the Embassy, this man Verloc gave us some very useful information. Later, I met him again. I told him that I knew he was a secret agent. He said he didn't want any trouble; he just wanted to look after his shop. "If you don't do anything wrong," I said, "you needn't worry about trouble from the police. Shops like yours are not usually safe from us, but yours will be. But if I help you, you must help me too." And so from time to time, when I want some information, he gives it to me.'

'But he didn't give you any information this time,' said the Assistant Commissioner.

'I didn't ask him anything, so he didn't tell me anything,' explained the Detective Inspector. 'My guess is that he knows nothing about this bomb.'

'Then how do you explain this?' asked the Assistant Commissioner, pointing to the burned piece of coat.

'I don't know. I don't understand it. I think that Michaelis will be able to tell us more about the bomb than Verloc.'

'You do? What about the other man, who escaped from the park in the fog?'

'He must be far away by now,' said Heat.

'I don't know. I don't understand it. I think that Michaelis will be able
to tell us more about the bomb than Verloc.'

The Assistant Commissioner thought for a short time. He didn't want to sit behind his desk; he wanted action. He sent the Detective Inspector away, and then he picked up his hat and left the office. He found a carriage and told the driver to take him to Brett Street.

Chapter 7   Sad News for Winnie

A few weeks before the Assistant Commissioner decided on his plan, Mr Verloc went to Europe to buy things for his shop. He was away for ten days. When he came back, he seemed tired. He walked into the shop and sat down immediately in a chair. Stevie was cleaning the shop. He stopped and looked at Mr Verloc in admiration.

'Here!' said Mr Verloc, and kicked his suitcase. Stevie ran over and took the suitcase upstairs.

Winnie heard the shop bell and she came in. 'You'll want some breakfast,' she said.

While he ate breakfast, Winnie talked to him about the shop. 'We had quite a few customers while you were away,' she said. 'Oh, yes, and I saw Michaelis two or three times. He told me that he's going to stay in Kent for a few weeks. He's going to write a book. And Karl Yundt visited once – terrible man.' She did not speak of Ossipon, but her face turned a little red. 'Stevie was unhappy while you were away. I don't mean that he wasn't useful round the house: he's always helpful. But he likes to see you and be near you. He admires you a lot. You only have to ask him, and he'll do anything for you.'

After breakfast Mr Verloc said, 'I'm going out for a walk.'

'Why don't you take Stevie with you?' asked Winnie.

Mr Verloc was surprised. It was a new idea. 'But if he loses me, can he find his way home?' he said.

'He won't lose you; he wants to be near you,' said Winnie. 'But I'm sure that someone will bring him back. You needn't worry.'

This was Mr Verloc's second surprise. Why was she so sure?

'All right. He can come with me.'

At the shop door, Winnie watched them. The two of them walked down the street, one tall and fat, the other short and thin. 'They look like a father and son,' she thought proudly.

Over the next few days, she was pleased to see that Mr Verloc seemed to like going out for walks with Stevie. Now, when he was ready to go out, he called to Stevie: 'Let's go!' They went out together every day. And in the house Mr Verloc watched Stevie. But Stevie sat in corners and talked to himself. She couldn't quite hear him. 'What are you saying, Stevie?' she asked, but he just looked angry and didn't say anything. She was worried. 'What do you tell him during your walks together?' she asked Mr Verloc.

'Oh, nothing, really,' said Mr Verloc. 'You wanted Stevie to come out for walks with me. Remember?'

The next day Mr Verloc said, 'I think Stevie needs a change. I'm going to take him to stay with Michaelis in Kent. Stevie will enjoy the fresh green trees and the animals.'

That day Stevie was more angry than usual. Winnie could hear some of the things he was saying: 'Bad world for poor people! Poor people must eat. If they're poor, perhaps they steal from rich people. Police hurt them, put them in prison.' On and on he went, sitting in his corner. She was worried, but she was pleased at Mr Verloc's kindness. It was good of him to take Stevie to stay with Michaelis.

On the day of the bomb in Greenwich Park, Mr Verloc went out very early in the morning and did not come back until nearly dark. She was sitting in the shop when Mr Verloc came in with the sound of the bell. She didn't look up from her work.

'The weather's bad, isn't it? Did you see Stevie today?'

'No, I didn't,' said Mr Verloc softly.

Some time later Winnie got up to go into the kitchen. 'Soon he'll want his supper,' she thought. But when she went into the back room, she saw that Mr Verloc was sitting by the fire.

'I think I've caught a cold,' he said.

'Did you get wet?' she asked. 'Where were you today?'

'Nowhere,' he said, but then a little later: 'I went to the bank. I took out the money.'

'What do you mean? All of it?'

'Yes.'

'Why?'

He didn't reply at first. She put some bread and cold meat on the table.

'Why don't you take off your shoes?' she said. 'They're all wet. You're not going out again tonight.'

Then he started to speak. 'Well,' he said, 'you see . . . I thought . . . I . . . if I suddenly have to go to France . . . I mean, go to live there . . . or California, perhaps.'

'That's a strange idea,' she said. 'Why will you have to go? The shop is doing all right. We're comfortable here.' She looked round the room. This was Stevie's home too. What about him?

Mr Verloc said nothing. Winnie came and gave him a kiss, but he sat in his chair without moving. She cleaned the table. His eyes followed her movements.

'If you go and live in France or somewhere,' she said, 'you'll have to go without me.' She was thinking of Stevie. He must stay here, in this country. 'But you won't go. You need me too much.'

Just then they heard the sound of the shop bell. 'Shop, Adolf,' she said. 'You go.'

Mr Verloc went into the shop. Winnie washed some cups and plates. He was a long time in the shop. 'It must be a customer,' she thought. She listened, but she couldn't hear voices.

'If you go and live in France or somewhere,' she said, 'you'll have to go
without me.' She was thinking of Stevie.

When Mr Verloc came back, his face was white. 'I have to go out,' he said. Winnie went into the shop and looked at the man who was waiting there. He was tall and well dressed. He didn't look like a customer.

She returned to the back room. Mr Verloc was putting on his coat. 'Who is that man?' she asked. 'Do you know him?'

'I've heard of him,' he said uneasily.

'He's not from the Embassy, is he?'

'Embassy!' Mr Verloc said in surprise. 'What Embassy? Who has said anything to you about Embassies?'

'You have, my dear,' she said. 'You were talking in your sleep.'

'What did I say?' Mr Verloc seemed frightened.

'Nothing sensible. But I knew that you were worried.'

'Those Embassy people!' said Mr Verloc. 'I want to cut their hearts out.' He pushed his hat on his head and started to go out.

'Adolf!' she called after him. 'What about the money? Give me the money.'

'Oh, yes,' he said. He gave her the money and she hid it among her clothes immediately, without looking at it. Then he went away with the visitor.

Winnie felt afraid. What was happening? Everything was mysterious and worrying. She felt danger all round her. Suddenly she heard the sound of the shop bell again. She went into the shop. A man was standing there.

'Is your husband at home, Mrs Verloc?' the man asked.

'No, he's gone out.'

'I'm sorry about that. I came to give him some information.'

This was true. When Detective Inspector Heat left the office, he went home, but then he decided to go to Brett Street. He wanted to warn Mr Verloc.

'When will your husband be back?' he asked. 'Do you know?'

'No,' she said.

'I'm Detective Inspector Heat of the police,' he said. 'Why did your husband go out? I want you to tell me.'

'I don't know,' she said. 'He went out with another man, a stranger.'

'Tell me about this stranger. What did he look like?'

Winnie told him. Heat's face turned darker. 'The Assistant Commissioner was quick,' he thought. To Winnie he said, 'I haven't got the time to wait for your husband now.'

Winnie said nothing. 'What do you know about this business?' Heat asked.

'What business? Nothing. I've stayed at home all day.'

'So you haven't seen any newspapers?'

'No.'

'Have you lost a coat – a coat with your address in it?' He showed her the piece of coat.

'That's my brother's coat. What do you mean?'

'Can I see your brother? Where is he?'

'He's not here. He's out of town, staying with a friend.'

'What's the name of this friend?'

'His name's Michaelis.'

Heat's eyes flew open in surprise.

'Interesting,' he said. 'And your brother – is he a big man with dark hair like yours?'

'No, he's short, with fair hair. But where did he lose his coat?'

Heat felt in his pocket for the piece of coat. He pulled it out and showed it to her. 'This is from my brother's coat,' she said. 'Who burned it like this?'

Heat sat down heavily in a chair. Now he knew that Verloc was the other man at the park.

'Mrs Verloc,' he said, 'I think you know more about this bomb than you think.'

They heard the sound of the bell. Mr Verloc walked into the shop. 'What are you doing here?' he asked the detective.

'I must talk to you,' Heat said. 'Come in here.'

They went into the back room. Winnie listened at the door. She could not hear everything that they said.

'You were the other man in the park, Verloc,' said Heat, and then a little later: 'Look! It has your address on it!'

'I didn't know,' said Mr Verloc.

'You must get away now,' Heat said. 'Go to Europe or somewhere. But how did you escape from the park?'

'I heard the bomb. It was too soon. I was waiting for him. I just ran away.'

'We think he fell,' the Detective Inspector said a little later. 'There were only bits of his body. You must go away.'

'Where will I go?' said Verloc. 'I told that other man, the Assistant Commissioner, that I wanted to stay and give a full report to the police. And I really do want to do that. I'm tired. I want to stay here with my wife, in this country, looking after my shop.'

Soon after that the Inspector left. Mrs Verloc sat in the shop, with her mouth open. She didn't cry; she didn't say a word. In her head she heard the words: 'Only bits of his body . . . only bits of his body.'

Chapter 8   Murder!

'She knows all about it now,' Mr Verloc thought. He looked at his wife. She was still sitting in the shop. 'She said to me, "You needn't worry." She said, "I'm sure that someone will bring Stevie home." Now I understand. She put the address in his coat. Why didn't she tell me?'

Mr Verloc went into the shop. 'I didn't mean to hurt the boy,' he said. 'It's all because of that terrible man at the Embassy.'

Mrs Verloc shut her eyes. She hid her face in her hands.

'Now, Winnie,' said Mr Verloc, 'we have to think of tomorrow. The police will come and get me. What will you do then?'

Mrs Verloc didn't move.

'Why don't you look at me?'

'I don't want to look at you as long as I live.'

'What? You don't mean that. Now, come out of the shop. You can't sit here.' There was no answer. He decided to try to be kind, instead of giving orders. 'This won't bring him back, you know,' he said.

Was she hearing him? He didn't know. He waited for a long time, but nothing happened. 'Don't be stupid, Winnie,' he said.

It was impossible to talk to a woman who was hiding her face in her hands. He held her hands and tried to pull them away from her face, but she kept her hands there and he pulled her off the chair. She ran into the back room.

After a time Mr Verloc followed her. First he turned off the gas lights in the shop and locked the door. He felt very tired. His work as a secret agent was at an end; he was on his way to prison.

'Why don't you go to bed?' he said. 'You need a good cry.'

While Mr Verloc went on and on, Mrs Verloc stood silently. Why was he talking? What was he talking about? Then a picture came into her head. Mr Verloc and Stevie were walking down the street together. 'They looked like a father and son,' she said.

'What? What did you say?' said Mr Verloc, but then he went on talking about someone at some Embassy. Winnie looked at the wall. She tried to remember something. What was it? Something terrible was happening. Then she remembered: 'This man took the boy away to murder him. He took the boy from his home to murder him. He took the boy away from me to murder him!' She hated him.

He didn't understand. She loved the boy with all her heart. She had to look after him. The butcher's son wanted to marry her, and she liked him, but he was poor: he couldn't pay for

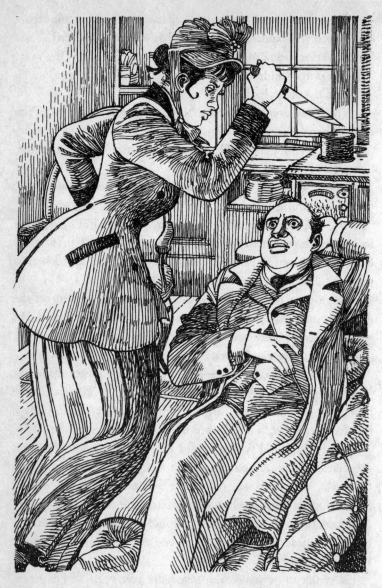

When she came to the sofa Mr Verloc opened his eyes.
She brought the knife down just once ...

Stevie. So she found Mr Verloc. She did everything for Stevie, and now Stevie was dead because of this man.

'You didn't know,' the man was saying. 'You brought the police here, with that address. But it's all right. I won't leave you. I like you too much.'

Mrs Verloc wanted to get away. She went upstairs. 'That's right,' he called out. 'You go and sleep'. But when she was upstairs, she only opened the window. It was not very far from the ground. She wanted to kill herself, but it was not high enough.

Mr Verloc felt very hungry. He cut some meat with a knife and ate it with some bread. He lay down on the sofa to rest. He could hear his wife upstairs. She was changing her clothes, he thought. When she came back downstairs, she was wearing her coat. Now she felt free.

'Where are you going?' Mr Verloc asked. 'It's too late to go out. You must stay here with me this evening. Why don't you talk to me? Say *something*, won't you?'

Mrs Verloc understood that she was not free. As long as this man was alive, she was not free.

'Winnie,' he said.

'Yes.'

'Come here.'

She walked over to the sofa. There was a knife on the table. She picked it up. When she came to the sofa Mr Verloc opened his eyes. She brought the knife down just once deep into his body and left it there. Mr Verloc died immediately.

She sat down. Now she was free. She didn't move, she didn't think. She was quiet, and the body of Mr Verloc on the sofa was quiet. He died without making a noise: no sound broke the respectability of their home. Everything was quiet and respectable.

She sat there for a long time, with her eyes on the ground. But then she looked up. There was a noise somewhere. What was it? She saw a black pool of something on the floor under the sofa. It was blood. Blood was dropping from Mr Verloc's side on to the floor.

Chapter 9   The Great Escape

Mrs Verloc quickly got up from the chair and ran out of the room. She unlocked the shop door and ran out into the street. She must be calm. She didn't want to die. 'I murdered my husband. They'll kill me,' she thought. 'I must escape. I must go to Europe.'

Out on the street she ran into the arms of a man. The man held her and looked at her. 'Mrs Verloc!' he said.

'Mr Ossipon,' she answered. 'What are you doing here?'

'I was coming to help you,' he said. 'Where were you going?' He still held her arm. Ossipon was not afraid of women. He had a lot of women friends. He was interested in women, and it was his luck always to find women. So he was not surprised to find Mrs Verloc in his arms.

'Perhaps I was going to find you, Tom,' she said.

Ossipon was excited that she called him 'Tom'. It was a personal name, used only by his best friends. 'I'm ready to help you,' he said.

'What do you know about my trouble?' she asked. He worried her.

'I read about the bomb in the newspaper. I met a man who gave me information. I knew that Mr Verloc was dead. Then I came over here. You know that I love you, don't you?'

'Yes, I know, Tom.'

'You've seen it in my eyes. But you never told me that you knew.'

'Of course not. I was a respectable woman.'

'I always thought that he was the wrong husband for you. But you seemed to live happily with him. You seemed to love him.'

'Love him!' she said. 'No, I didn't love him. I wanted my brother to be as comfortable as possible. I never loved my husband.'

'But he's dead now.'

She put her hand on his arm. 'You know that he's dead?'

Ossipon didn't understand. What was this woman talking about? Of course he knew that Verloc was dead.

'How did you first hear about it?' he asked.

'From the police.'

'The police were here already?'

'Yes. They showed me a piece of coat. And there was another man too. Perhaps he was from the Embassy . . .'

'Embassy? What Embassy?'

'I don't know. Don't ask me questions, please, Tom. I'm tired.'

'All right,' Ossipon said. 'I won't.'

'You must hide me somewhere until the morning,' she said. 'Then we can go to Europe together.'

'But I have no money,' said Ossipon.

'Don't worry. I have plenty of money,' she said. 'He gave it to me.'

Ossipon thought, 'Who gave it to her?' But he didn't ask her. He said, 'I think we're all right. There's a boat at midnight and a train from Waterloo station at 10.30. We can catch that train, and by the morning we'll be in France!'

'I think that I left the light on in the house,' she said. 'Will you turn it off for me?'

'Is the money in the house?' he asked.

'No, I've got it on me. Please . . . just go and turn off the light in the back room. I don't want anyone to see it.'

She pushed him inside and he walked through the shop into

139

the back room. First he saw Mr Verloc's hat in the middle of the floor. Then he saw the dark pool of blood. His eyes moved towards the sofa ... He turned back into the shop and was sick. Was this a trap? What was happening? He ran towards the shop door, but just then Mrs Verloc came inside.

'There's a policeman on the street,' she said quietly. 'I think he saw me. If he comes in, you must kill me. You will, won't you?'

But the policeman walked on past the house. After a few minutes Ossipon and Mrs Verloc left the shop. They found a carriage which took them to Waterloo. 'They mustn't catch me,' Winnie said, 'I don't want to die. I'll stay with you for ever. I ... I won't ask you to marry me.'

'Was he asleep?' Ossipon asked.

'No, he was talking. He took the boy away to kill him. He killed the boy and then he lay quite easy on the sofa. "Come here," he told me. Do you hear, Tom? he said, "Come here," after taking my heart along with my poor boy. Help me!' she cried. 'You must help me!'

'When we arrive at the station,' he said, 'you must get on to the train before me. I'll meet you there. Nobody must see us together. Clear?'

'Yes.'

'Give me the money now. I'll buy the tickets. Here we are now, at the station. Go on. Get on the train. I'll come in a minute.'

'There's no danger, is there, Tom? I'll be safe?'

'Yes, perfectly safe, my dear. Don't worry about a thing.'

He bought the tickets and found her on the train. 'Oh, Tom,' she said. 'How can I thank you? I was afraid, but you've helped me. I'm not afraid now. I'll live for you always, Tom.'

When the train started to move, Ossipon got up. He opened the door and jumped out on to the platform. He fell down and people came over to him. 'Are you all right?' they asked. He picked himself up and laughed. 'Yes,' he said. 'There's no problem. My sister was crying, and I stayed too long on the train to look after her. But I'm not hurt. Do you see? I can walk.' And he left the station, laughing quietly to himself.

◆

A few days later he was drinking beer with the Scientist in the same pub. In his pocket was a newspaper. Some words from the newspaper were running through his head. 'A mystery,' the newspaper said. 'Why did the young woman throw herself off the ship to France? Why did she kill herself? What trouble was she in?' Ossipon hated himself.

ACTIVITIES

Chapters 1–3

Before you read

1 What is a secret agent? Use your dictionary to find out. What sort of work do they do? Can you think of a very short word in English which means the same as 'secret agent'?

2 Find these words in your dictionary.

action admire carriage

Which word means:

a something with four wheels which is pulled by horses

b to think a person is good or important

c something that you do

3 Find these words in your dictionary.

anarchist bomb revolution

The story in this book happens in England in the 1880s. There were quite a lot of *anarchists* in Europe in those days. What do you know about anarchists? Tell another student. Then write two sentences about anarchists with the following words: *revolution, bomb*.

4 Find these words in your dictionary.

bell Embassy respectable trap

Now use the words to finish these sentences.

a An ..... is the office of a foreign country in your country.

b A ..... is something which catches people or animals.

c A ..... makes a musical sound.

d A ..... person is someone who seems to do the right things.

After you read

5 Who are these people? Put the names on the left with the words on the right.

a	Mr Verloc	works in a foreign Embassy.
b	Mr Ossipon	is Mr Verloc's pretty young wife.
c	Mr Vladimir	owns a small shop.
d	Stevie	is one of Mr Verloc's friends.
e	Winnie	is Winnie's problem brother.

6 At the anarchists' meeting, Michaelis says, 'In the end the workers will win and a new golden time will begin for man.' Do you agree with this? Why/why not?

Chapters 4–6

Before you read

7 What do you think Mr Verloc is going to do? Do you think he *can* put a bomb in the Greenwich Observatory? Why/why not?

8 Find these words in your dictionary.
   explosive   foggy
   a What sort of people use *explosives*? Why? When? Where?
   b What is the weather like in your country? Is it ever *foggy*? What sort of accidents can happen when it is foggy?

After you read

9 Answer these questions:
   a What is strange about the Scientist's room?
   b What news does Ossipon tell the Scientist?
   c What is Stevie carrying when he goes into the park?
   d Where is Michaelis living when he is writing his book?
   e Who does the Detective Inspector want to save? Why?
   f What is the address of Mr Verloc's shop? Why is this address on Stevie's coat?

10 People still use bombs today to frighten and kill others. Think of reasons why people do this.

Chapters 7–9

Before you read

11 Look at the picture on page 136. What is the woman with the knife going to do? Why?

After you read

12 Who says these words? Who to?
   a 'Those Embassy people! I want to cut their hearts out.'
   b 'There were only bits of his body. You must go away.'
   c 'I don't want to look at you as long as I live.'
   d 'If he comes in, you must kill me.'

13 Work with another student. Have a conversation.

Student A: You are Mr Verloc. You are out walking with Stevie. Tell him what you want to change in the world.

Student B: You are Stevie. Ask Mr Verloc questions about what anarchists think and do.

Writing

14 Tell the story again through Winnie's eyes. How does she live? Does her husband seem strange to her? What are her feelings for Stevie? What does she feel after she hears about the bomb?

15 You are the policeman who finds the dead body in the park after the bomb. Write a report. What do you do? What do you see? Who do you talk to?

16 No one in *The Secret Agent* is happy or good. Even the policemen are just trying to help their friends. Do you think that Conrad gives us a picture of the real world? Why/why not?

17 Did you find the story exciting? Did you always want to ask, 'What will happen next? Who has died in the park? How does Conrad keep the story exciting?

Cranford

ELIZABETH GASKELL

Level 3

Retold by J. Y. K. Kerr
Series Editors: Andy Hopkins and Jocelyn Potter

Contents

Introduction

Here it is the women, not the men, who make the rules. If you want to know what to eat or what to wear or who to have to your party, you only need to ask one of the Cranford ladies.

This story is about life in a small town in the north-west of England during the 1840s. It is about little Miss Matty and how she lost nearly all her money: about Signor Brunoni and how he became a conjuror; about why Miss Matty's younger brother Peter ran away from home; and, most of all, it is about the ladies of Cranford. There are no bad people in Miss Matty's world: there is only kindness and friendliness between neighbours.

Elizabeth Gaskell was born Elizabeth Stevenson in London in 1810. Her mother died when Elizabeth was just a year old, and one of her aunts took her to her own home in the small town of Knutsford, in Cheshire. Elizabeth remembered the years growing up in Knutsford and wrote about them much later in *Cranford*. She had a brother, John, who was twelve years older. When Elizabeth was eighteen, he disappeared at sea on a journey to India, and this brought great sadness to the family. (The return of a lost sailor is part of the story in many of her books, but John never returned.) When Elizabeth was visiting relatives in Manchester, she met William Gaskell, a churchman like her father. They married in 1832 and decided to make their home in Manchester. They had six children but two of them died very young.

Elizabeth began to write after the death of their only son, William. In 1847 she wrote three short stories. Her first book, *Mary Barton*, came out in 1848. It was about factory life in the north of England. Charles Dickens, the famous writer, read it and immediately invited her to write for his weekly magazine,

Household Words. Elizabeth wrote five other books. *Cranford* (1853), *North and South* (1855) and *Wives and Daughters* (1866), which was unfinished at her death, are the best known. Many of her books first appeared in weekly parts, as chapters in magazines like *Household Words*. But Elizabeth did not like having to write a chapter every week. Finally she ended her agreement with Dickens.

In 1850, she met the famous writer, Charlotte Brontë, and they became great friends. After Charlotte's death in 1855, her father, Patrick Brontë, asked Elizabeth to write his daughter's life story. She agreed and *The Life of Charlotte Brontë* came out in 1857. It was very popular. As well as writing, Elizabeth looked after her four daughters and, with her husband, she spent a lot of time helping the poorest people in Manchester. She decided to use some of her money from writing to buy a house in the country. She wanted this to be a surprise present for her husband – a family home for them. In 1865, while on a visit to this house in Alton, Hampshire, she suddenly became ill and died. She was fifty-five.

Elizabeth Gaskell's books are about a number of different subjects. *Cranford* describes the lives of middle-class women in a peaceful country town. *North and South* shows the differences between life in a big city and life in the country. Like Charles Dickens, she wrote about the problems of factory workers. This was not a popular subject in the middle of the nineteenth century. All her books have a lot to say about the position of women, especially poor women. For example, *Ruth* (1853) is about the difficulties of a seventeen-year-old girl who is a single mother. In *Sylvia's Lovers*, an innocent, good-hearted woman has to marry a man she does not love because she believes that her lover is dead. Many of Elizabeth Gaskell's subjects are still important for readers today. But *Cranford*, with its group of simple, warm-hearted ladies, is still her best-known and best-loved book.

Chapter 1   The Ladies of Cranford

My name is Mary Smith and I am twenty-eight years old. My mother is dead and I live with my father, a businessman in the big city of Drumble in the north-west of England. But this story is not about Drumble or about my family. It is about a small town where I lived when I was a child and the people who still live there. The name of this place is Cranford.

In many ways Cranford is quite an ordinary place, where few exciting things happen. But in one way it is very special. Here it is the women, not the men, who make the rules. If you want to know what to eat or what to wear or who to have at your party, you only need to ask one of the Cranford ladies. For example, the ladies of Cranford think that it is very important to visit newcomers. You must always do this on the second day after the newcomer arrives and you must visit between the hours of twelve and three. Then the newcomer has to repay the visit in the next three days. These visits must be short: never for more than quarter of an hour. You must not talk about anything that matters because there isn't time and, most importantly, you must not talk about money because that is a subject for business people, not for people of good family. Of course, all the Cranford ladies are of good family, or think they are, which is almost the same thing.

Another strange thing about Cranford is that there are not many men about. Of course, there is Dr Hoggins and the Rector* of the church; and then there are shopkeepers and farmers and people like that. But these men are not part of the real life of Cranford, which belongs to the ladies and only to them. You see, most of the ladies do not have husbands. Either they are unmarried or their husbands are dead. In fact most of these ladies are quite old and they are not

* The Rector is the head of the church in a small town or village.

very interested in men – or that is what they tell us. 'A man in the house gives so much trouble.' That is what the Misses Jenkyns thought, or more truly, that is what they said.

I want to tell you about these two old ladies because they have been friends of my family for many years. When I visit Cranford, which is about four times a year, I nearly always stay at their house, where I can be sure of a warm welcome. Miss Deborah and Miss Matilda are the daughters of the Reverend Jenkyns. He was the last Rector of Cranford Church – I mean the Rector before the one who we have now. Mr Jenkyns has been dead for many years but both the ladies are very proud of their father and always speak of him lovingly and with great seriousness. Neither Miss Deborah nor Miss Matty (as most people call her) is married but they are important people in the little world that is Cranford. I have heard that Miss Matty did have a male friend when she was young but we shall return to that subject later. Miss Deborah is the one who looks after the house and the money and gives all the orders: she is one of those strong people who knows that she is always right. Miss Matty is quite different – loving, sweet and shy. She is often unsure about all sorts of things and prefers to follow her older sister's rules. They are both good people and everyone in Cranford loves them.

About this time a new family came to live in the town. Captain Brown served as a soldier for most of his life. He was now over sixty years old and had a desk job with the railway that ran through the neighbourhood of Cranford on its way to Drumble and the north. His wife was dead and he had two daughters, both unmarried. The first one, Miss Mary, was about forty years old and was always in bad health, which made her look much older than she really was. Her sister Jessie was about ten years younger and twenty times prettier than her sister, with clear blue eyes and soft brown hair. She spent all her time looking after Mary, doing everything possible to make her sick sister's life pleasanter.

Captain Brown and his daughters lived in a small house just

outside the town. They had very little money but the Captain made no secret of being poor. Of course the Cranford ladies thought that this was shocking. As I have explained, one of their rules was never to talk about money, and it was unthinkable to talk about not having enough. The Captain again surprised everyone when, one winter's day, he helped an old woman by carrying her Sunday lunch home for her because the streets were icy. In Cranford a gentleman did not do this! The ladies waited for him to explain himself but the good Captain did not seem to think that there was anything to explain. He was kind and helpful to everyone, telling Miss Betty Barker what to do when her cow got sick, showing Miss Pole how to stop her sitting-room fire from smoking; so that after some time all the Cranford ladies agreed to forgive his strange ways and asked him and his daughters to their card parties and musical evenings.

But then something truly terrible happened to the Brown family. One afternoon Miss Deborah, looking out of her window, saw small groups of townspeople talking together in the street, so she sent her servant Jenny to ask what was happening. Jenny returned in a few minutes, crying and frightened, her face white.

'Oh, Miss Deborah, Captain Brown is dead! It was one of those terrible railway trains that killed him!'

Hearing this, Miss Matty immediately ran out into the street and found the man who brought the news. Soon the railway worker was standing in the Misses Jenkyns's sitting-room.

'Did you see this terrible accident?' asked Miss Deborah.

'Yes, ma'am.'

'Then please tell us what happened.'

'The Captain was at the railway station reading a book and waiting for the train to arrive. Suddenly a little girl escaped from her mother's hand and began to walk across the railway line. Just then the Captain looked up and saw the train coming. He ran on to the line, caught up the child in his arms and threw her up to her

153

*One winter's day, he helped an old woman by carrying
her Sunday lunch home for her.*

mother. But then his foot caught on something and he fell under the train and now he's dead, poor man! They've gone to tell his two daughters the sad news.'

We were all deeply shocked. Miss Deborah looked ill and troubled but she went for her hat at once, saying: 'Matilda, I must go to those girls. They need help.'

Some hours later she came back home, sad and silent. Finally she told us what happened. 'Miss Jessie nearly died of shock,' she said. 'She asked Miss Pole and me not to say anything about the accident to her sister. "Doctor Hoggins thinks that Mary doesn't have long to live," she said. "I'm afraid that this news will kill her." So we didn't tell Miss Mary what happened. She thinks that her father has taken a short journey on railway business and is away for a few days.'

Miss Pole offered to go and stay with Miss Jessie to help her through this difficult time. The next day the full story was in the local newspaper and Miss Deborah asked me to read it to her. When I finished reading, Miss Deborah shook her head sadly and said, 'Poor, dear man. How kind he was. How brave!'

Miss Jessie wanted to follow her father's body to its last resting place and none of the ladies could stop her. So Miss Deborah decided to walk with her to the church. She put her arm round Jessie's shoulder while she was saying her final goodbye to the father that she loved so dearly.

The next day Miss Jessie was again calm and strong. She thanked each one of us with a sad smile. By now it was clear that her sister Mary was dying. Miss Pole and Miss Deborah went to help nurse the sick woman. Mary's last thoughts were of her dear sister and father, and of the great love that she felt for each of them.

'Mary,' her sister said softly, 'our father has gone before you to the place where you and he will rest. Soon you will be together. He knows how much you loved him.'

Now that both the father and sister were dead, Miss Deborah wanted Miss Jessie to come and stay at her house, knowing that

Miss Deborah put her arm round Jessie's shoulder while she was
saying her final goodbye to the father she loved so dearly.

Jessie had very little money. But just then a gentleman arrived in Cranford; he was an old friend of Captain Brown and he knew Miss Jessie when she was a sweet young girl of eighteen. This Major Gordon was a fine tall man, about forty years old. He had land in Scotland and so he was quite rich. He loved Miss Jessie and some years before he asked her to marry him; but at that time, knowing how much her sick sister needed her, Miss Jessie could not agree to be his wife. Now here he was again, repeating the same question, and this time Miss Jessie felt able to say yes. In a few weeks they were married and went to live in Scotland.

After she left Cranford, Miss Jessie did not forget her old friends. The two Jenkyns sisters and Miss Pole all went to stay with the Gordon family at different times and came home with wonderful stories of Jessie's house, her husband, her dresses and her beautiful little girl, Flora. In later years little Flora came to stay with Miss Deborah and Miss Matty in Cranford and was almost like a daughter to them. So the sad story of the Brown family had a happy ending for one of the three.

Chapter 2   An Old Love Story

The years went by and Miss Deborah Jenkyns also died, to the great sadness of her many friends. But I continued to visit Cranford, staying sometimes with Miss Pole or more often with Miss Matty. On one of these visits Miss Matty's servant Fanny decided to leave and Martha, a new young woman, came to take her place. In looking after the house, Miss Matty followed all Miss Deborah's rules; but when she had to decide anything for herself, she felt deeply worried and was frightened of making mistakes. She asked me to help her teach the new servant the ways of the house. This Martha was a girl who grew up on a farm. She was hard-working and very honest and she had a kind heart; but she was also a little rough in her ways. She took a long time to learn the house rules. For example, we had to show Martha how to serve food at table.

'You must offer the potatoes and the vegetables first to the ladies and then to the gentlemen,' Miss Matty explained, when her married cousin from India was coming for a meal.

'I'll do everything that you say, ma'am,' said Martha, 'but I must say that I like the men best.'

It was at this time that I first learned about Miss Matty's love story. Her friend Miss Pole had a cousin who lived four or five miles from Cranford. His name was Thomas Holbrook and strangely he did not live like a fine gentleman. He preferred the life of a farmer, wearing old clothes and speaking like the local people. He was a great lover of books and read from them beautifully, with great feeling. He was very much in love with Miss Matty in the old days, Miss Pole said.

'So why didn't Miss Matty marry him?' I asked.

'The rest of her family thought Thomas's family wasn't good enough. You see, she was the Rector's daughter. Thomas asked her and I think she wanted to marry him but in the end she said no.'

'Did she ever see him again?'

'No, I think not,' answered Miss Pole. 'You see, Thomas's house is halfway between Cranford and Misselton. After Miss Matty gave her answer, Thomas always went to Misselton to do his shopping and has only come to Cranford two or three times since then. Once I was out walking with Miss Matty, and when she saw him coming, she ran away and hid.'

'How old is he now?' I asked, hoping that this was not the end of the love story.

'Oh, he's about seventy, I think,' said Miss Pole, breaking my beautiful dream in pieces.

Not long after this conversation, I was with Miss Matty when Mr Holbrook made one of his few visits to Cranford and met his old love again. We were in a shop, Miss Matty and I, looking at some new cloth in different colours which she needed to brighten up an old dress. Just then a tall thin man came in, asking for coloured handkerchiefs. I never saw him before. I watched carefully while Miss Matty was talking to the shopkeeper. When she heard his voice, I saw her jump. Then she sat down very suddenly.

I guessed immediately who the stranger was. Hearing Miss Jenkyns's name spoken, Mr Holbrook quickly came across to us.

'Matty, Miss Matilda, Miss Jenkyns! How are you? How are you?' he called out, and he shook her hand warmly. 'I didn't realize it was you.'

He kept talking to us, waving the shopman to one side with the words 'Another time, my friend, another time.' He walked all the way back to Miss Matty's home with us. Miss Matty was just as surprised as he was. It was lovely to see Mr Holbrook's happiness at meeting his old love again. He spoke of the many changes in their lives.

'We have lost your poor dear sister,' he said sadly. 'Dear Miss Deborah.'

Finally he said goodbye but spoke of his warm hope of seeing Miss Matty again before long.

As soon as we got home, Miss Matty went at once to her room and didn't come out again until teatime. When she finally took her place in her favourite chair, I noticed that her eyes were red from crying.

A few days later, a letter came from Mr Holbrook, asking us both to spend a day at his house. He also wrote to Miss Pole. To my surprise, we had great difficulty in getting Miss Matty to agree to go. Finally we pushed her into saying yes and I wrote to tell Mr Holbrook that we were coming. So one Thursday the three of us started out in a borrowed carriage, because it was too far to walk. After some time we came to a pretty house with a garden full of roses, standing by itself among fields.

'My cousin needs to make a carriageway up to the front door,' said Miss Pole, while we were making our way on foot through the sweetly smelling garden.

'I think it is very pretty just like this,' said Miss Matty quietly.

Mr Holbrook showed us round the place. He had some fine farm animals. While we walked, he spoke lines from poems that he knew. In the kitchen we sat down to a well-cooked meal. After eating, we left him to smoke his pipe. We ladies sat in the sitting-room, full of dancing tree-shadows. There were books everywhere: on the floor, on the table, round the walls.

'What a pretty room!' said Miss Matty.

'It needs a good cleaning,' said Miss Pole. 'Why does he have so many books?'

'Your cousin has always been a great reader,' said Miss Matty.

When Mr Holbrook came in, he asked us to go for a walk in the fields with him but the older ladies were afraid of getting their feet wet. So he took a short walk with me. When we got back, he offered to read us some poems. I noticed that Miss Matty's eyes began to close during the reading. I am sure she was asleep; but when he finished, she woke up quickly and said, 'How pretty.'

'Pretty, ma'am? You mean beautiful,' said Mr Holbrook. 'I will buy you a book for you to keep, because I know you too enjoy poems.'

Finally it was time to go home. Mr Holbrook walked with us to the carriage. 'I'll call on you quite soon,' he said, waving goodbye.

When we arrived home, Martha met us at the door. It was already dark. 'Oh ma'am, you've been out so late wearing only that thin coat, and at your age! What were you thinking of?' she said.

'And what is my age?' asked Miss Matty, with a little smile.

'I think you are nearly sixty, ma'am,' said Martha.

'Oh, Martha, I'm not yet fifty-two,' said Miss Matty in a hurt voice.

After our visit to the old farmhouse, Miss Matty never spoke about Mr Holbrook but I was watching her carefully and I could see that her heart was still true to him.

Mr Holbrook offered to read us some poems.

Mr Holbrook kept his word and soon came to visit us. 'Can I bring you anything from Paris?' he asked. 'I'm going there next week. Oh, and Miss Matty, here is the book of poems that I promised you.'

Soon after this I had to leave Cranford and return to Drumble but I asked Martha to write to me if she thought that Miss Matty needed anything. I did get a letter from time to time. Then suddenly the news came that she was very downhearted and was eating very little. I decided to see for myself. My visit came as a surprise but I got a warm welcome. Miss Matty really did look ill.

'She has been like this for two weeks,' Martha told me, 'ever since Miss Pole came to see her.'

'And are you happy here, Martha?' I asked.

'Yes, miss, only that I can't have a young man. There's Jem Hearn, a very nice boy who's interested in me. But I promised Miss Matty not to have men friends and I had to send him away.'

When I spoke to Miss Pole, I learned that her cousin Thomas was very ill. It seems that the illness began after that journey to Paris. 'He hasn't been round his fields once since he came back. He just sits at home with his hands on his knees, talking about Paris. Dr Hoggins says that he has not got long to live,' she said.

'Does Miss Matty know?' I asked.

'Oh, yes. She has known for two weeks. I'm surprised that she hasn't told you.'

Miss Pole came to visit her old friend and I left them together. Later, I heard that Miss Matty had a bad headache and was in her room. She came downstairs at teatime and talked a lot about her dead parents and sister, their kindness and goodness and how much she missed them.

The next day Miss Pole brought news that Mr Holbrook was dead. Miss Matty heard the news in silence. I could see that she was shaking and couldn't speak. In the days that followed, she tried to hide how sad she felt by never talking about Mr Holbrook; but I noticed that his book of poems was always on her bedside table.

One evening, Miss Matty was very silent and thoughtful. She asked Martha to come to the sitting-room.

'Martha,' she said, 'you are young.'

'Yes, ma'am. Twenty-two last October.'

'I did say you were not to have followers. But if you meet a young man that you like and if you tell me about him, and if I think he's a good man, I'm ready to change the rule that I made. He can visit you once a week. I don't want to stand in the way of young loving hearts.'

'Well,' said Martha, 'there's that Jem Hearn who is six foot tall and a wonderful woodworker, getting good pay every week. If you ask about him in the town, everyone will tell you he's a very good young man. I'm sure he'll be very happy to come and call on me tomorrow evening, thank you kindly, ma'am.'

Miss Matty was greatly surprised at this reply; but she understood better than most people the importance of love when your heart is still young.

Chapter 3   Poor Peter

One evening we were sitting in the dark, waiting for Martha to bring the lamp and the tea. Miss Matty went to sleep and then woke up suddenly with a strange look on her face. She began to talk about her early life and her father and mother. She disappeared upstairs and came back with a big box of family letters, yellow with age. There were letters from her father to her mother before they got married and letters from her to him. There were also letters from Miss Deborah when she went to stay with friends in the north of England. Miss Matty was specially proud of these letters and read them to me one by one. Finally there were letters written by her father to his son Peter when Peter was at school in Shrewsbury, and Peter's letters to his parents in reply. It was soon clear that Peter

163

Miss Matty read these letters to me one by one.

often got into trouble. He was usually saying he was sorry for his mistakes. One very short, badly written letter said:

My dear, dear, dear, dear, dearest Mother,
  I will try to be a better boy. Don't be unhappy and get ill because of me. I am not good enough, I know, but I will be good, dearest Mother.

On seeing this piece from the past, Miss Matty felt so sad that she silently gave me the letter to read and began to cry quietly. Later she took this letter to her bedroom to keep it safe, unlike the other letters, which she and I burned in the fire, one at a time.

'Poor Peter!' she said. 'He was always in trouble. Other boys pushed him into it. He loved a joke, that was all. Poor Peter!'

Until then I did not realize that Miss Matty had a brother. Another evening, when she was calmer, I asked her to tell me Peter's story.

'His father wanted him to study at Cambridge and then go into the church,' Miss Matty explained, 'but that did not happen.'

'And was he a bad student?' I asked.

'No, that was not the problem,' answered Miss Matty. 'The trouble with Peter was that he was a joker. He loved to play tricks on the people of Cranford. Some of his jokes were very shocking. Once he dressed up in women's clothes and said he was a lady visiting the town. After church he asked to speak to our father, to tell him that he was a wonderful church speaker. Father was very pleased, of course, and wanted to give her some of the other talks he was specially proud of. In fact he asked Peter to write them out for her! He never guessed that the unknown lady was really his son and that it was all just a joke. And then a terrible and very sad thing happened.'

Before telling me more, Miss Matty sent for Martha and asked her to go for eggs to a farm on the other side of the town. Clearly she wanted to keep this story as secret as possible.

'I'll lock the door behind you. You're not afraid to go, are you, Martha?' she said.

'No, ma'am. I'll ask Jem Hearn to go with me.'

Miss Matty then began her story.

'One day, when Deborah was away from home and our father was out visiting some sick people, Peter went to Deborah's room and dressed up in her coat and hat – the clothes that she usually wore in Cranford. Then he took a pillow and made it into the shape of a little baby wearing long white clothes. Then he walked up and down in the garden, talking to the baby in the way that mothers do. Soon a crowd of people was standing in the road outside, watching him and thinking that he was Deborah. When our father came home, he was very surprised that all these people were looking in at our garden. Suddenly he understood what was happening and got very angry. He pulled the clothes off Peter's back and threw the pillow on the ground. Then he began to hit Peter as hard as he could with a piece of wood. When he stopped for a rest, Peter said quietly, 'Have you finished with me, Father?' Then Peter turned and waved to the people who were watching and walked slowly into the house. He went straight to our mother in the kitchen and said, 'I have come to say I love you and will love you for ever.' He put his arms round her and kissed her and before she could speak, he turned and left.

My mother soon learned what happened and went to Peter's room to talk to him but Peter wasn't there. We looked for him all over the house, calling his name again and again. Our mother went on looking in the same places all afternoon but she found nothing. Our father sat with his head in his hands, terribly unhappy, not saying a word. Of course we were all afraid of the same thing: of Peter killing himself.'

'Where was Mr Peter?' I asked.

'He ran away to Liverpool and got work as a sailor. The captain of his ship later wrote to my parents, telling them to come at once to Liverpool to see Peter; but the letter arrived late and when father and mother got to Liverpool, the ship was already on its way to India. Our mother missed Peter terribly. She said very little but Peter's disappearance was a very great sadness and this sadness

He walked up and down in the garden, talking to the baby
in the way that mothers do.

slowly killed her. Naturally we didn't realize this at the time. She got weaker and weaker, and she thought more and more of the things that she wanted to say to him. By now we all knew that the end was near. She did not live a full year after Peter left home. And just think, on the day that she died, a packet came from India with a big white Indian cloth made of fine wool – just what she always wanted. We put it round her after she died and I remember thinking that she seemed to have a smile on her face.

Our father was never the same after our mother died. I think it broke his heart.'

'Did Mr Peter ever come home?' I asked.

'Yes, once. He was "Captain Jenkyns" by that time. Our father was so proud of him. He took Peter to every house in Cranford. They were great friends.'

'And then?'

'Then he went to sea again. Soon after that our father died and our lives changed. We couldn't stay on in the big Rector's house with four servants. So we moved to this small house and now we have only Martha to look after us.'

'And Mr Peter?'

'Oh, there was some big war in India. We have never heard of him since then. I'm sure he's dead. But sometimes when the house is quiet, I think that I hear the sound of his feet coming along the street and my heart goes faster; but the feet always go past without stopping and Peter never comes.'

Just then we heard a knocking at the kitchen door. 'There's Martha back,' said Miss Matty. I'll go and unlock the door for her. I find this room much too warm, Mary, don't you?'

Miss Matty left the room. Five minutes later she returned, her face looking a little pink.

'Was it Martha?'

'Yes, and I heard the strangest noise just when I was opening the door. It seemed to me like the sound of . . . the sound of . . .'

168

'I heard the strangest noise just when I was opening the door.
It seemed to me like the sound of . . . the sound of . . .'

'Talking?' I said.

'No, kissing!' replied Miss Matty, and her lips had the shadow of a smile on them.

Chapter 4   The Great Brunoni

Soon after this I had to leave Cranford and return to Drumble because my father was ill. I did not have news of my Cranford friends for nearly a year. Then in November I got an excited letter from Miss Matty. The first thing was that she wanted me to buy her a turban – one of those hats that Indian men make out of long pieces of cloth – because she heard that well-known people were wearing them that year. The second thing was to ask me to pay her a visit because Signor Brunoni, the famous conjuror, was giving a special show at the Cranford Assembly Rooms that week. She did not want me to miss it.

I was very happy to visit Miss Matty again but did not think that a great big Indian turban was right for her sweet little face. She was pleased to see me but sorry that I brought her one of the little hats that she usually wore instead of the much wanted turban.

That evening Miss Pole came round specially to tell us all about her visit to the Assembly Rooms earlier in the day. 'They were full of workmen who were preparing the lights and the furniture for tomorrow night,' she said, in her knowing way. 'While I was look-ing round, a gentleman who was speaking a very pretty kind of foreign English came and asked if I wanted anything and, when I said no, he showed me out of the room. When I went downstairs, someone told me who the foreign gentleman was – Signor Brunoni, the conjuror! Just then he came downstairs and spoke to me again, so I thought it was time to leave.'

So Miss Pole was the first among us to see the famous man.

'Is he young or old?'

'Is he dark or fair?'

'How does he look?'

Miss Pole spent half the evening trying to answer our questions.

Mrs Forrester was also coming to the show. She was sure that some people were special, able to do strange things that ordinary people do not understand. Miss Pole preferred to look for facts as an explanation. Miss Matty was undecided. After tea they sent me to look for a book about conjuring and Miss Pole studied it so fully that she forgot all about the game of cards that the rest of us were waiting to play. Every five minutes she read out bits from the book:

'A is the ball. Put A between B and D – no, between C and F, and turn the third finger of your left hand over the back of your right hand. You see, Miss Matty, it's perfectly clear.'

Finally we did have our card game but only because Miss Matty gave the book to Miss Pole to take home with her.

The next evening we were all ready a long time before the show. When the doors of the Assembly Rooms opened at seven o'clock, Miss Matty walked in with her head held high, remembering the dances that she enjoyed here when she was young. We sat right at the front. Soon Mrs Jamieson and Lady Glenmire were with us, so we were six. Other people came in and sat behind us but Miss Pole said quickly in my ear, 'Don't look round. It is not the thing to do.' It seems that this was another of the Cranford ladies' rules.

After a lot of waiting, the show began and we saw a wonderful gentleman in richly coloured clothes sitting at a little table. He had a dark beard and a big Indian turban on his head.

'You see, people *are* wearing turbans this year,' Miss Matty said to me softly.

'That's not Signor Brunoni,' said Miss Pole in a loud voice. 'Signor Brunoni hasn't got a beard. Perhaps he'll come soon.'

But the man got up and gave his name in very broken English as the Great Brunoni in person. Mrs Jamieson woke up from her sleep (she fell asleep very easily at all sorts of parties and other

171

We saw a wonderful gentleman in richly coloured clothes sitting at a little table. He had a dark beard and an Indian turban on his head.

happenings), Miss Pole stopped talking for a little and we all watched Signor Brunoni's wonderful tricks. Miss Pole kept looking at a piece of paper she had with her, which explained the tricks, and she went on reading from it in a loud voice. Signor Brunoni looked at her angrily but this did not stop her. The rest of us were very surprised and pleased at all the tricks he did for us.

Miss Matty and Mrs Forrester were beginning to think that it was not quite right to watch all these mysteries, so Miss Matty asked me, because I was not a person of the town, to look round and see if the Rector was also in the room. She felt that if the Rector was there, there was no need to worry. I looked and there he was, sitting with a group of schoolboys. He was a tall thin man and people said he was very afraid of women. If he saw one of the Cranford ladies coming down the street, he ran into a shop and hid. At one time people thought that Miss Pole was interested in him; but at the end of the show he gave our group a friendly wave and Miss Pole looked the other way, not wanting to notice him. She was still repeating loudly that the man in the turban was not Signor Brunoni but someone quite different. So ended our evening with the great conjuror.

For several weeks after the Great Brunoni's show, there were stories of robberies, disappearances and other strange happenings in Cranford. I read a report in the newspaper that someone saw the shape of a headless lady when walking one night in Darkness Lane. Miss Matty got frightened very easily by stories like this, and she began to look under her bed at night before getting into it, to see if there was a man hiding there. I'm glad to say she never found one.

Chapter 5   The Story of Sam Brown

Again several months went by and again I was making one of my visits to Miss Matty at Cranford. Going for a walk one morning, I met Lady Glenmire and Miss Pole starting to cross the fields outside the town. They were planning to visit an old woman who made very good woollen socks. I decided to go with them. We were not sure of the right way to take, so we asked at The Rising Sun, a little pub on the London road. The wife of the pub-keeper kindly asked us to come inside and rest a little, while she went to ask her husband. Just then a beautiful little girl, called Phoebe, came into the room and Lady Glenmire began talking to her. When the pub-keeper's wife returned, she explained that she was not the child's mother and told us a very strange story. Six weeks before, a carriage carrying a big box had an accident just outside their door. One of the carriage wheels broke in several pieces. Travelling in the carriage were two men, a woman and this little girl. One of the men hurt himself badly in the accident and they brought him into the pub and put him in one of the bedrooms. He was too ill to move, so the man's wife stayed to look after him and the other man mended the broken wheel and then went off in the carriage. Miss Pole asked about the sick man.

The pub-keeper's wife replied, 'He's not really a gentleman and he's not really a working man. He's more like a person in the theatre business. The two men are brothers,' she went on, 'and it's difficult to know one from the other.'

Finally we learned to our great surprise that the sick man was in fact Signor Brunoni, and that his real name was Sam Brown. We continued to call him the Signor because it had a better sound but he was no more Italian that I was! From now on the ladies of Cranford decided to look after the Signor and nurse him back to health. Lady Glenmire went to see Dr Hoggins and asked him to ride over and listen to the poor man's heart. Miss Pole promised to find the family somewhere to live in Cranford and paid for it personally. Miss Jamieson sent her carriage to move him and his family to their new home. Mrs Forrester called almost every evening with dishes of food and Miss Matty brought boxes of playthings for little Phoebe. We were so busy with all this good work that we forgot all about the robberies, the missing people and the headless woman of Darkness Lane.

♦

One day Signora Brunoni told me their family story.

'I never find it difficult to know which brother is which,' she explained. 'They do look almost the same but my Sam is a much better conjuror than Thomas. I must tell you that Thomas is a very good, kind person. We were able to pay for our stay at the pub with the money that he's sent us. But he's never been in India and still doesn't know the right way to wear a turban.'

'Have *you* been in India?' I asked in great surprise.

'Oh, yes, for many years. You see, Sam was a soldier and I followed him there. I was happy to be with him but I must tell you, ma'am, that I lost six children in that unhealthy country. Every time one died, I felt that I could never love another. But another came and then it died also. When Phoebe was on the way, I said to my husband. "Sam, when this child is born and I'm strong again, I'm going to leave you. I'll go to Calcutta and somehow I'll pay for my ticket home to England." He agreed, so that is what I did. I walked most of the way to Calcutta and kind people sometimes carried me a part of the way and helped me by giving me money and food. The poorest people, when they saw that I had a baby, often gave me presents of rice or sweets or fruit.'

'But you arrived at Calcutta safely at last?'

'Yes, I got a place as a servant to an English lady in bad health who was going home to England. And two years later, Sam got free of his soldier's life and came home to me and our child. That's when he began his conjuring – he knew a lot of tricks which he learned from Indians over the years. He asked his brother Thomas to help him and Tom has learned some of the tricks, too. The great likeness between the two brothers has helped some of the tricks to

'I walked most of the way to Calcutta.'

work very well when they do them together. But still I can always tell which is Sam and which is Tom.'

'Poor little Phoebe! How far she has travelled!' I said, thinking of the hundreds of miles that her mother carried her across India.

'It's true,' said the Signora, 'and once I very nearly lost her, when she fell ill at Chunderabaddad; but that good kind Aga★ Jenkyns took us into his house and saved her life.'

'Jenkyns? Did you say Jenkyns?' I asked.

'Yes, that was his name,' the Signora answered. 'The same name as the kind old lady who comes to take Phoebe for walks.'

An idea suddenly came into my head. Could Aga Jenkyns and 'poor Peter' possibly be the same person? I decided to do everything that I could to find the answer to that question. I needed more information; but every time that I asked a Cranford lady about Peter Jenkyns, I got a different answer. One thought he was good-looking, another thought he was ugly, one remembered him as dark, another as fair-haired, and so on. The only thing that everyone agreed about was that 'he was probably in India or that part of the world'.

We were so busy talking about the past that we didn't notice something happening right under our noses. One day Miss Pole arrived at Miss Matty's door, shaking with excitement, to say that Lady Glenmire and Dr Hoggins were planning to get married. We all liked Lady Glenmire and felt happy for her; but we were not so sure about what Mrs Jamieson felt about it. Lady Glenmire belonged to Mrs Jamieson's family – everyone thought they were the best family in Cranford – and Mrs Jamieson made no secret of the fact that she did not think Dr Hoggins a real gentleman or his family in any way good enough for hers. Luckily, she was away from Cranford for some days at the time.

'Do you think she'll be pleased when she hears the news?' Miss Pole asked Miss Matty.

★ *Aga*: an Indian word used for an important man, the head of a family.

'Oh dear! No, I think not,' was Miss Matty's reply and of course she was right. Mrs Jamieson stopped speaking to Lady Glenmire as soon as she got the information.

But the idea of a wedding in this sleepy little town was exciting and started us thinking about new clothes. We were happy to learn that the best clothes shop in Cranford was having a show of all the new spring dresses during the coming week: a great help in our planning what to wear at the wedding.

Chapter 6   Stopped Payment

One Tuesday morning, two letters arrived at breakfast time. One was from my father. In it he asked if Miss Matty still held shares in the Town and Country Bank, because there was a story going round that the bank was closing down. Years before, he warned Miss Matty's sister, Deborah, not to put any money into this bank but clearly Deborah did not listen.

'Who is your letter from, dear?' asked Miss Matty. 'Mine is from the heads of the Town and Country Bank. They're asking me to go to a sort of party for the shareholders in Drumble next Thursday. How kind of them to remember me.'

I did not like the sound of this offer but I said nothing to Miss Matty, thinking that bad news usually travels fast.

Instead we decided to go shopping early with the idea of buying half a pound of tea. In this way we could also look at the cloth for the new dress which Miss Matty was planning to make for the Glenmire–Hoggins wedding and perhaps see the new spring dresses before too many of the other ladies arrived.

The young shopmen were ready to show us everything. Miss Matty spent a long time trying to decide between a lovely rose-coloured cloth and a sea-green one. Next to her was a young farmer choosing a present for his wife. Finally he chose the thing that he liked best and offered a five-pound note to pay for it. The shopman studied the banknote very carefully – it was a Town and Country Bank note. Then he said, 'I'm sorry but we have only just learned that this bank is in serious difficulties and from now on we are unable to take any of its banknotes. Can you please pay some other way?'

Miss Matty was very interested in this conversation. I tried to bring her back to the problem of choosing a piece of cloth for her new dress but it was no use.

'Young man, I'll give you five pounds in gold for that note,' she said to the farmer. 'I think that there has been some mistake; but I'm one of the bank's shareholders and I'll take the problem to the heads of the bank when I visit them next week. Everything will soon be clear, I'm sure.'

'But what if they give us bad news?' I said, feeling very uncomfortable.

'If I'm a shareholder, I must pay for the bank's mistake,' answered Miss Matty calmly.

The farmer looked at her thankfully and Miss Matty decided to come back to choose her cloth another day. Looking at the spring dresses on show upstairs, we saw Miss Pole across the room but decided that it was not a good time to start a conversation. When we were leaving the shop, the young shopman ran after us and personally warned Miss Matty against having anything more to do with the Town and Country Bank. 'Their banknotes are quite useless now,' he said, with a wave of his hand. 'Don't touch them, ma'am.'

We walked home, neither of us saying a word. After dinner Miss Matty sat at her desk and looked through her bank papers. After some time she shut the desk and came over to sit with me. I put my hand in hers. She pressed it hard but did not speak. At last she said in a shaky voice, 'If that bank closes, I'll lose nearly all my money. I'll only have £13 a year to live on. I'm so glad that dear Deborah didn't live to have these worries. She was a very proud person, you know.'

'Young man, I'll give you five pounds in gold for that note,'
she said to the farmer.

I could only press her little hand, not knowing what to say.

Late that night I sat down and wrote to the Aga Jenkyns, telling him everything that was happening to his sister. It was the only thing that I could do. If he really was Peter, he was sure to reply.

The next morning the news came that the Town and Country Bank was stopping all payments. For Miss Matty this was the end. She cried a little, not for herself but for her servant. 'Poor Martha,' she said, 'I think she'll be sad to leave me.'

While Miss Matty went to tell Martha the bad news, I escaped from the house and posted my letter to the Aga Jenkyns. When I got back, Martha opened the door for me, crying loudly into her handkerchief.

'I'll never leave her, no I won't! I've got some money in the bank and I've got enough clothes, so I'm not going to leave Miss Matty – ever!'

♦

Miss Matty, when I found her, was very quiet and a little sad. She wanted me to write to my father, asking him to pay her a visit, and I agreed. I tried to think of ways in which Miss Matty could work and get money to live on but she was not a teacher or a writer or a businesswoman. The important thing was that any work that she did had to be 'good enough for a lady'.

Later that same day Martha came in with her young man, Jem Hearn the woodworker. 'We have a plan,' she said. 'Jem and I are going to get married. Then we'll find a house to live in and have you, Miss Matty, to stay with us.'

Jem was a man of few words but he spoke some of them now to Miss Matty. 'I'm thankful to anyone who has been kind to Martha and you have been the kindest lady that ever was. I hope that you'll agree to live with us, ma'am. We'll do our very best to make you comfortable.'

The next morning Miss Pole, looking very mysterious, asked

'You have been the kindest lady that ever was. I hope that you
will agree to live with us, ma'am.'

me to come over to her house, where a group of Miss Matty's closest friends were waiting to talk to me. They were greatly worried about how little money she had and had an idea for helping her. Each lady wanted to give some money every year to pay for her living costs but of course Miss Matty must never know about their plan. I thanked them all warmly and agreed to keep the secret.

When my father arrived, I was able to tell him about the ladies' kind offer. In the end we decided on the following plan. Jem and Martha agreed to live in Miss Matty's house. Miss Matty paid them a little money every week for her room and her food. Miss Matty then sold all her furniture and got some more money that way. (I learned later that her friends bought some of her favourite things and then gave them back to her, much to her surprise.) But the best idea of all was to make the front room of the house into a little shop. Here Miss Matty sold tea to the people of Cranford. Miss Matty was unsure about this idea at first but in fact she was quite good at shop-keeping. She was afraid of male customers because they counted the money much faster than she could and because they spoke in loud voices; but few men came. The thing that she liked best was visits from children and she kept a big box of sweets specially for them!

In this way Miss Matty's life was again calm and happy.

Chapter 7   A Happy Homecoming

The ladies of Cranford continued to visit Miss Matty and bought their tea at her shop. Mrs Jamieson was strongly against Lady Glenmire and Dr Hoggins getting married but seemed to find Miss Matty's work as a tea-seller perfectly all right for a Cranford lady. Both Dr and Mrs Hoggins looked wonderfully happy at their wedding the next Sunday and Jem and Martha looked just as happy at their wedding a week later.

The room that Miss Matty used as the shop was bright with new paint, and the words 'Matilda Jenkyns, Seller of Tea' stood over the shop door in gold letters. Miss Matty sold much more tea than anyone thought possible and in fact made quite a lot of money, but she gave away too many free sweets to her younger customers. I came to see her about every three months, to help with her business letters. I spoke to no one about my letter to Mr Jenkyns. By now I was sure it had disappeared on its long journey to India, or arrived at the wrong address, because no reply came.

About a year went by and then suddenly I got a very badly written letter from Martha, asking me to come to Cranford as soon as possible. I was afraid that Miss Matty was ill, so I left home that same afternoon. But the news which Martha had for me was much happier: her first baby was coming in a week or two. The problem was that Miss Matty didn't realize that the baby was near and so Martha wanted me to tell her the good news.

'I don't think she'll like the idea, miss,' said Martha, 'and I don't know who will look after her when I'm in bed having the baby.'

'I'll stay and help until you're able to get up again,' I said. 'Don't worry, everything will be all right, you'll see.'

I left the house by the back door and went round to the front, to the shop, meaning to surprise my dear old friend. The weather was warm and the shop door stood open. Miss Matty was sitting making a pair of socks and singing to herself in a low voice. She stood up to serve me, not realizing at first who I was. But suddenly she dropped her wool with a little shout of happiness and threw her arms round my neck. What Martha said was true. I soon understood that she had no idea of the arrival of the baby. So I decided to leave things to happen in the most natural way. A week later, I again went round to see Miss Matty in her shop, this time with a little baby girl in my arms. Miss Matty was highly excited. Together we looked lovingly at its beautiful little face and hands and feet.

While Martha was in bed getting back to health, I had a busy time cooking our meals, doing Miss Matty's paperwork, looking after the baby and sometimes helping in the shop. When children came to buy sweets, which happened several times a day, I found that Miss Matty always gave them more than they paid for. Really, it was hard to understand how the shop could make any money.

Life in Cranford went on in the usual way. Mrs Jamieson was still turning her back on Dr and Mrs Hoggins: but they were newly married and did not seem to notice anything wrong. Martha was up again and back at work, often with her little girl, Matilda, in her arms. Then one afternoon, when I was sitting in the shop with Miss Matty, we saw an old gentleman go slowly past the window and then stop opposite the door. He put on his glasses and read Miss Matty's name above the door. Then he came into the shop and I said to myself, 'Surely this is Aga Jenkyns!' because his face was brown from the sun and his clothes had a foreign cut. He looked hard at Miss Matty, then at me, then at Miss Matty again. She was a little worried at having a male customer in the shop. The stranger suddenly said to me, 'Is your name Mary Smith?'

'Yes,' I answered.

I could see that he wanted to tell Miss Matty his name but did not want to give her too great a shock.

'Kindly give me a bag of those things there,' he said, pointing to some expensive sweets on the table. Something about his face brought back a remembrance of past times to her heart.

'Oh dear! . . . is it . . . are you . . . can you be Peter?'

By now poor Miss Matty was shaking from head to foot. Immediately Peter took her in his arms and she was crying like a child.

'I have been too sudden for you, Matty, my dear little sister,' he said. It was true. Her face lost all its colour and she was almost unable to speak, so I told her to lie down and gave her a glass of wine. Then I ran to tell the good news to Martha in the kitchen and together we got the tea things ready.

Miss Matty sat opposite Mr Peter at the teatable and could not

'*Kindly give me a bag of those things there,*' *the stranger said,*
pointing to some expensive sweets on the table.

take her eyes off him. He brought out a dress and some rings which were presents for her from India. Miss Matty picked up the dress lovingly and said softly, 'But now I am too old. Oh, why can't I be young again?'

Peter wanted to stay at a hotel but Miss Matty told him he must not. I gladly gave him my room and moved my things to Miss Matty's room. I left brother and sister deep in conversation and went to make up the bed for the homecomer. Later that night when Miss Matty and I were in bed, she retold some of Peter's adventures: how he fought foreign enemies and ended up a prisoner; how he escaped by saving the life of an Eastern king; how the letters that he sent to England came back with the word 'Dead' on them; how he then decided to stay in India and try his luck as a farmer and businessman. This is where Signora Brunoni met him and where he finally got my letter.

In the middle of the night I woke to find Miss Matty climbing out of bed and disappearing from our room for a few minutes.

'I'm sorry, my dear,' she said when she returned. 'I just went to look at Peter. I wanted to be sure that he is really here.'

A day or two after Mr Peter came home, they closed the shop, giving the tea that was left as presents to the Cranford ladies. The beautiful Indian dress went to Miss Flora Gordon, Jessie Brown's daughter, because the Gordon family too was coming back to live in Cranford.

♦

The house now looked like it did before, with no shop and the empty rooms full of furniture again. Jem and Martha and little Matilda (Miss Matty's name of course) continued to live in the house and to look after Miss Matty and her brother. It was time for me to return to my home in Drumble.

But not for long. A month or two later I got two letters on the same day. Miss Matty and Miss Pole each wrote, asking me to come

*I saw Mrs Jamieson beside Peter, and she was listening happily
to every word that he said.*

and meet the Gordons again, because they were now back in England with their children almost grown up. Mrs Gordon (who was Jessie Brown before she got married) wanted to see her old friends in Cranford and was inviting us all to a lunch party at the George Hotel. 'And not only that,' wrote Miss Matty, 'dear Peter is also planning something special for us but he wants it to be a surprise.' And Miss Pole wrote, 'The big question is this, Mary. If the Hogginses come to the party, will Mrs Jamieson also agree to come?' None of us was sure of the answer to that question.

'Leave Mrs Jamieson to me,' said Mr Peter on the day of the lunch. And when we were all at table, I saw Mrs Jamieson beside Peter, and she was listening happily to every word that he said. 'Could these be words of love?' I asked myself. But no! When I walked past their places, I realized that Peter was playing his old tricks again, telling the good lady of his wild and wonderful adventures in the East. He looked at me, closed one eye and said softly, 'This is my way of keeping her happy – and keeping her awake!' We drank the health of everybody in the friendliest way: Mrs Jamieson, Dr and Mrs Hoggins, Major and Mrs Gordon, Miss Pole, Miss Matty and Mr Peter. Then Mr Peter got up to tell us of the surprise that he planned for that evening. He was inviting us all to a special conjuring show by the Great Brunoni!

That night he entered the Assembly Rooms with Mrs Jamieson on one arm and Mrs Hoggins on the other. And so all was well between the two families in the end.

So now Cranford is a friendly, quiet place again. And dear Miss Matty, a person who loves goodness and kindness more than anyone, is our perfect example. I think we are all better people when she is near us.

ACTIVITIES

Chapters 1–2

Before you read

1 When do you think the things in this story happen?
   a 15 years ago
   b 50 years ago
   c 150 years ago
   How do you know?

2 All these words come in this part of the story. Use a dictionary to learn their meaning.
   carriage   cloth   gentleman   lady   servant   shocking
   Now choose the best meaning for each word.
   a a woman from a good family
   b used for travelling before we had cars
   c used for making clothes
   d a person paid to work in another person's house
   e gives you a very bad surprise
   f a man from a good family

After you read

3 What are the names of these people?
   a Miss Matty's older sister
   b the last rector of Cranford church
   c Captain Brown's older daughter
   d Miss Jessie Brown's husband
   e Miss Pole's cousin
   f Martha's boyfriend

4 Answer these questions:
   a How does Captain Brown die?
   b Where do Miss Jessie and her husband go to live?
   c How do Miss Matty and Thomas Holbrook meet again?
   d Why did Miss Matty decide not to marry Thomas Holbrook?

Chapters 3–5

Before you read

5 In this part of the story, do you think that Miss Matty will get married? Say why or why not. Talk about this with other students.

6 These words all come in this part of the story. Use a dictionary to learn their meanings.

conjuror joke pillow tricks turban

Now use the words to complete these sentences:

a The dog has learned some clever . . . . . .

b The . . . . . pulled a white bird out of his hat.

c Rest your head on this . . . . . .

d Men in India often wear a . . . . . on their heads.

e He told us a . . . . . that was very amusing.

After you read

7 Answer these questions:

a Who dresses up in women's clothes? Why?

b Who hits Peter with a piece of wood? Why?

c Whose face goes a little pink after she unlocks the door? Why?

d Who wears a turban? Why?

8 Who said this? Who to?

a '. . . then a terrible and very sad thing happened.'

b '. . . I love you and will love you for ever.'

c 'But you arrived at Calcutta safely at last?'

Chapters 6–7

Before you read

9 Miss Matty has shares in a bank. To *have shares* means:

a to keep important papers

b to own small parts of

c to hold money for another person

10 A piece of paper money is called a . . . . . . (The answer comes in Chapter 6.)

11 How do you think the people of Cranford live today, 150 years after

Mrs Gaskell wrote her book? What are their rules? How do they spend their time? Discuss these questions with other students.

After you read

12 Where does Miss Matty:
   a offer a young man some gold? Why?
   b open a little shop? What does she sell there?

13 Who is the 'old gentleman' who comes to Miss Matty's shop one afternoon? What happens to Miss Matty's life after he comes?

14 Who invite their friends to the George Hotel? Why? And what happens in the evening after this party?

Writing

15 In Chapter 1, Mary Smith reads in the local newspaper how Captain Brown died. You are the reporter and you saw what happened. Write a report.

16 Peter Jenkyns loves to talk about his dangerous adventures in the East – 'how he fought foreign enemies and ended up a prisoner; how he escaped by saving the life of an Eastern king.' Write the story of one of his adventures.

17 You are Mr Holbrook when he was young. Write a short love letter to Miss Matty.

18 Write a short note to a friend about this book. Give an idea of the story. Say if he or she will like the book, and why or why not.

Silas Marner

GEORGE ELIOT

Level 3

Retold by A. J. Brayley
Series Editors: Andy Hopkins and Jocelyn Potter

Contents

Introduction

George Eliot's real name was Mary Ann (Marian) Evans. She was born in 1819 in Warwickshire, England. When her mother died, in 1836, she had to look after the family home. She continued her studies, though, with the help of visiting teachers, and became very interested in religion. She and her father had important differences of opinion about religion, but she looked after him until his death in 1849. In 1851 George Eliot went to London and worked on a magazine called *The Westminster Review.* There she met George Henry Lewes. They fell in love with each other and lived in Germany and London until his death in 1878. They were not able to marry, because Lewes was already married. At that time he could not, by law, end his marriage. This was a problem for Eliot and Lewes; many people had strong feelings about a woman living with a married man. Slowly, though, their friends began to accept the situation. After Lewes died, George Eliot married John Walter Cross, who was much younger than her. She died the same year, in December 1880. After her death, Cross produced her *Life, Letters and Journals.*

George Eliot was already interested in writing fiction when she was a schoolgirl. But she did not start writing professionally until 1856. Her first stories, *Scenes of Clerical Life* (1858), were very popular. Many people thought that they were written by a churchman. Her first longer work, *Adam Bede* (1859), was also highly successful. Eliot described it as "a country story" and it gives a clear picture of everyday life in the country at that time. *The Mill on the Floss* (1860) and *Silas Marner* (1861) followed. Her greatest book is believed by many people to be *Middlemarch* (1871–2). In this story readers follow the activities of people of every class in the town of Middlemarch. Eliot's last great work of fiction was *Daniel Deronda* (1876). She also wrote a lot of poems.

Her books were popular with all kinds of readers; one person who enjoyed her stories was Queen Victoria.

Silas Marner is shorter than most of Eliot's books and is probably the best known. In England under Queen Victoria there were big differences between classes of people. The message of the book, though, is that love is greater and more important than class or money. The story and its message were popular in those days and are popular today.

Silas Marner is a weaver. As a result of his unhappy past he has no confidence in other people. He lives alone in the village of Raveloe, without love or friends. The most important thing to him is the money that he makes from his work. He saves this at home and counts it every night. But he cannot hide from other people completely. His life is changed by the actions of Dunstan and Godfrey, the two sons of Squire Cass. Godfrey has a secret. Dunstan knows about it and makes his brother's life very unhappy. By chance Silas, too, becomes important to their story.

PART ONE

Chapter 1   The Weaver of Raveloe

As a young man, Silas Marner lived in a big town. He was a weaver and his friends were also weavers. They all went to the same church, in a place called Lantern Yard. At that time Silas Marner had a strong love of God and he went to church every Sunday. He was a good and honest man.

His best friend in Lantern Yard was William Dane. William was older than Silas and he, too, seemed a very fine young man. But William more often forgave his own faults than those of other people. And he saw everyone's mistakes except his own. Even his teachers at school were sometimes wrong. But William Dane was always right.

Silas loved this young man and found no fault in him. He liked the fact that William was sure about everything. Silas was less sure of himself. He worried about his own faults. This difference between them showed in their faces. Silas's eyes shone with love but saw little; they were open and honest and almost too kind. William had a more secretive look in his narrow eyes.

One day Silas met a girl by the name of Sarah. Soon he was in love with her and he wanted to marry her. She loved him and promised to become his wife. But they could not marry yet because they needed more money.

Sometimes Silas brought William with him when he met Sarah. There was no fear in his heart. He loved them both and he wanted them to be friends. Then, one day, a bag of money was stolen from the church. Silas's knife was found in the church, so his house was searched. It was William who found the empty bag behind a cupboard in Silas's bedroom.

'It *was* you,' William said to his friend angrily. 'Tell the truth now!'

This hurt Silas deeply. 'William,' he said, 'I did not take the money. We are old friends. In nine years, I never once told you a lie. God will show us the truth.'

'Silas,' William replied, 'how could I know all your secrets? Sometimes a man seems honest, but deep in his heart he is bad.'

Silas looked at his friend. He was red in the face, and angry words were ready to pour from his mouth. But something stopped them. The red turned to white and his legs almost failed him. Finally he spoke in a low voice.

'I remember now. The knife wasn't in my pocket.'

William said, 'I know nothing about that.'

The other church people wanted to know more, and asked a lot of questions. But Silas did not explain his words. 'I am in great trouble, but I can say nothing,' he told them. 'God will show you the truth.'

They returned to the church. They did not call in the police; that was not their way. 'But we have to find out the truth,' they all agreed. First they fell on their knees and asked God for help. Then one of the church people offered two white cards to Mr Paston, the minister. On top they were the same. But one had a mark on the other side of it. The minister had to choose one of the cards.

'God will guide his hand. The minister will take the clean card,' said Silas to himself. 'But how can a man − a friend − behave so badly? I shall never forget that.'

Mr Paston chose one of the cards and held it up. It was the one with the mark. He spoke in a cold, hard voice. 'Silas Marner, you have done a terrible thing. You do not now belong to our church. You can only return to it if you give back the money. You will also have to say that you are sorry. And you will have to change your way of life.'

*It was William who found the empty bag behind a cupboard
in Silas's bedroom.*

Silas listened without a word. He stood up only when the others started leaving their places. He went to William. He spoke with great difficulty.

'I remember that day when you wanted a knife. You used mine and you never gave it back to me. *You* took the money. You lied about me to protect yourself. But do not be afraid. God will not hurt *you*. He hurts only the good. He, too, is a God of lies.'

The church people never forgot these terrible words, but William replied calmly. 'You should not speak like that. But I shall only say "God forgive you", Silas.'

Silas left the church. It was the end of the world that he knew. Dark thoughts drove all love out of his heart. Because he was not a clever man, he stopped believing in a loving God.

'God has turned away from me,' he thought. 'Sarah will, too. If she does not, she will not be happy either. How can we be happy if God hates us?'

At home he sat alone. He was like a sick man; he could do nothing. He did not even want to see Sarah. 'She will never believe me. She won't be able to accept the truth, so she won't believe me,' he said to himself.

The next day he was working at his loom when the minister brought a message from Sarah. She did not want to marry Silas or to see him again. Silas said nothing. He turned back to his work.

Little more than a month later Sarah married William Dane. Silas left the big town and moved to the village of Raveloe.

He lived there quietly for the next 15 years. He lived and worked in a small house outside the village next to an old quarry. Nobody took stone from the quarry now, so it was full of water. Few of the villagers went near it. Silas was known as a very strange man, and they were rather afraid of him.

Chapter 2   Love of Money

The village people knew nothing about Silas's secret. They were afraid of him for other reasons. He never invited them to his house, and he never drank with the other men in the village bar. The noise of the loom interested some of the village boys at first. They stood and listened outside Silas's house. When Silas saw them, he stepped down from his loom. He opened the door and, without a word, he fixed his large brown eyes on the boys. He looked hard at them because he could not see very well. But the boys did not know this. They ran away in fear. They knew from their mothers and fathers that Silas could help sick people. He had skills which were greater than those of other men. But when he was angry, there was danger in his eyes.

To add to his strange eyes, there was another mystery about Silas. Jem Rodney met him one evening at his gate and told his story later in the village bar.

'He was standing close to the gate. But he wasn't resting; there was a heavy bag on his back. His eyes were like a dead man's eyes. His arms and legs were as hard as stone. I spoke to him, and put my hand on him. He didn't move. "He's dead!" I said to myself. Then suddenly he was himself again. "Good night," he said, and walked away.'

The villagers talked about this and they also, for a time, discussed his skills with the sick. One day Silas took an old pair of his shoes to the house of Mr Oates, the shoemender. Sally, Mr Oates's wife, was sitting by the fire. She looked very ill and Silas saw the signs of heart trouble. He felt sorry for her because he remembered the same terrible signs in his mother before her death. He remembered the name of the plant that slowed his mother's illness. He said to Sally, 'The doctor hasn't helped you. I believe that I can. I'll bring you something.'

After a few days Sally Oates was much better. There was a lot of talk in the village. Soon all kinds of people were coming to Silas's house. There were mothers and their children and men from the farms. They all brought money. But Silas refused it. He was an honest man. Most of them wanted help which he could not give. He told them this, but they did not believe him. They continued to come. In the end he became angry and he drove them away.

And so Silas's kind act did not in the end bring him closer to the village people. They were angry with him too. After that nobody went near his house and they left him quite alone.

But Silas was not interested in the village people. He was only interested in his work. He worked all day and far into the night. His troubles hurt him less when he worked hard. And because he was alone in the house, there was work of another kind. He cooked his own meals. He lit his own fire and carried water from the well. In this way he drove out all thought from his life. He hated the past. He felt no love towards the people of Raveloe. He was without friends and without God.

Because he worked so hard, he earned a lot of money. He was the only weaver in Raveloe and he was paid for his work in gold and silver coins. He spent little on himself, but slowly his interest in the gold and silver grew. Every new pound made him happy for a short time, but then he wanted more. The coins were like friends and they seemed to know him. Every night he took them out and counted them. He loved their shape and colour and their shining faces.

Their home was in a metal pot under his loom. He took some stones out of the floor and made a hole. Each night, after counting the coins, he returned the pot to the hole. Then he put back the stones, and covered them with sand. This was not because he was afraid of thieves. Many country people saved their money and kept it in their houses. But nobody stole from their neighbours. They were not all honest, of course, but what could a thief do with the stolen money? He could only spend it in some other part of England.

Year followed year, and Silas continued to live alone. He worked and slowly filled the metal pot with coins. He watched them; and he worked. That was his life. No other thought, no other person had any part in it. The loom changed the shape of his back and of his arms and legs. When he left his work each evening, he could not stand up straight. He was not forty years old, but his face was dry and yellow like an old man's. The children called him "Old Master Marner".

But love was not quite dead in his heart. Every day he brought water from the well. He carried it across two fields in a brown pot which he bought specially for this purpose. The pot always stood in the same place. He felt happy when he touched it. When it was full, the water had a fresh, clear look. After 12 years it was like a friend. And then one day he dropped it. It broke into three pieces. With a heavy heart Silas stuck the pieces together. The pot was no use, but he put it in its old place. He wanted to remember it the way it was.

Fifteen years is a long time, but Master Marner's life showed little change. He spent all day at work. At night he closed his doors and took out his money. Because the metal pot could not hold it all, he moved the money into two thick leather bags. Out came the gold and silver pieces. How cheerful they were! There was more gold than silver and he loved the gold pounds best. He spent the small silver coins on his own needs. He pushed his hands through the piles and counted every coin. He enjoyed feeling the shape of the coins between his thumb and fingers. 'And these are not all,' he said to himself. 'Others are on their way, like children not yet born. Year will follow year, and they will continue to come.'

But soon a second great change came to Silas's life.

At night he closed his doors and took out his money.

Chapter 3   The Sons of Squire Cass

The most important man in Raveloe was Squire Cass. He owned a lot of land with several farms on it. Men who lived and worked on the farms paid the Squire rent for them. So the Squire was quite rich. But his wife was dead and he preferred the village bar to his own house. His sons got into bad company and soon learned bad ways. All rich young men enjoy themselves but these two never did any work at all. The fault, the village said, was the Squire's; he did not teach them to behave.

Nobody liked the second son. His name was Dunstan but everybody called him "Dunsey". He was a rude young man who said terrible things about other people. He lied, and he drank like a fish.

Godfrey, the older son, was different. At first he was kind and honest. Everyone liked him. He wanted to marry Miss Nancy Lammeter and the Raveloe people were pleased by this.

'He'll be a good squire when his father dies,' they said. 'And she'll be a good wife. They're a fine pair and she'll look after his money for him.'

Then Godfrey went away for a time. When he returned, he was a different person. His face no longer had its fresh colour and its honest look. Sometimes he was angry without reason. He was clearly hiding some kind of secret.

'He's following the bad example of his brother,' people said. 'If he continues like this, Miss Lammeter won't marry him.'

One winter afternoon, Godfrey was alone in a dark room in his father's house. Clothes lay on chairs or on the floor. Dirty silver cups stood on the table and the fire was smoking. Godfrey was waiting for someone and there was an angry look on his face.

The door opened. A young man with a thick, heavy body came in. His face was red with drink and he was smiling for no reason. Godfrey gave him a look of hate. Godfrey's dog hurried away from the fire and hid in a corner.

'Well?' Dunsey asked. 'What do you want?'

'It's about Fowler,' Godfrey said angrily. 'You remember – he paid me his rent and I gave it to you. Now the Squire wants that money. If he doesn't get it this week, he'll go to the police. Then the true story will come out and you'll be in trouble.'

Dunsey's smile grew wider but his eyes were hard. 'You'll be in trouble, too,' he said. 'The Squire won't like your story about me but he'll like my story about you even less. Don't forget – you married Molly Farren. I didn't. She's not exactly a nice young woman. And she leads a very ugly life. And now you hate her. What will the Squire do if he hears that? You'll have to leave the house. All his money will come to me.' He smiled again and his voice changed. 'But if you're nice to me, I won't tell him,' he said. 'You'll have to pay him Fowler's money. You'll get that hundred pounds, won't you?'

'How can I?' Godfrey cried. 'I haven't got any money. And you won't take my place here, either. If you talk, I'll talk too. Then we'll both have to leave.'

'No, we won't. You won't be so silly. You'll get the money and the Squire will have his rent.'

'I can't get the money!' Godfrey shouted.

'Sell your horse, Wildfire.'

'That'll take time. I need that money now.'

'Ride him to the hunt tomorrow. You'll get an offer for him there.'

'I don't want to come back late with dirt all over me. I'm going to Mrs Osgood's dance.'

'Aha!' Dunsey laughed. 'You want to see sweet Miss Nancy, do you?'

Godfrey's face was very red. 'Be quiet about Miss Nancy or I'll hit you!' he said angrily.

'Why?' asked Dunsey coldly. 'Let's talk about Nancy. Perhaps you'll be lucky. Molly may not live long. Then Nancy can be your second wife. That won't trouble her because she won't know. I won't tell her your secret. I won't tell her if you stay friendly with me.'

'Listen!' cried Godfrey angrily. 'I've had enough of this. If you continue, I shall tell the Squire everything. Then you can't trouble me any more. Perhaps Molly will tell him that she's my wife. She said that once, when she was angry. Now she'll be even more angry. I can't give her money because you take it all. But I'm not paying your price any more. I'll tell my father everything. Keep the secret or don't keep it. It doesn't matter to me.'

Dunsey was afraid now but he did not show it. 'Please yourself,' he said. He sat down and put his feet on another chair. Godfrey stood over him and his hands opened and closed. He was thinking hard. His body was large and strong and he was never afraid of a fight. But in matters of right and wrong he was less sure of himself.

He was very frightened at this moment. No plan could get him out of all his difficulties. After a little thought, he decided that he did not want to tell his father everything. He was angry with Dunsey but he was more afraid of the Squire.

'What can I do, if my father drives me out?' he asked himself. 'I hate working. I'll lose Nancy. But I can't give up my drink and other entertainments. Dunstan will always want money from me. But even that is better than life with no money or fun.'

Suddenly he spoke in an angry voice. '"Sell Wildfire", you say in your unfeeling way. I never had a better horse. What will people think?'

Dunsey smiled. 'Send me to the hunt tomorrow. I'll sell Wildfire for you.'

'And run away with the money! No, thank you!'

'Please yourself,' said Dunsey quietly. 'It's not my business. You

Godfrey stood over him and his hands opened and closed.

took the money from Fowler and lied to the Squire about it. I only wanted to help you.'

Godfrey walked angrily away. Then he came back. 'All right!' he cried. 'Sell Wildfire and bring me the money! If you don't, it is all over for you. In fact, we are both finished.'

Dunstan got up. 'You're being very sensible. I'll talk to Bryce. He'll pay a hundred and twenty pounds for the horse. You'll see.'

'And don't drink too much tomorrow, or you'll fall off. I'm not worried about you, but I am worried about Wildfire,' Godfrey told him.

'Don't trouble yourself. I never drink too much if I'm selling something. And I shan't hurt myself if I do fall.'

Dunstan closed the door noisily and left. Godfrey's thoughts returned to the reason for his problems. His sadness was greater because he was in love with Nancy Lammeter. She offered him everything: a good and happy life, a way of leaving his uncomfortable home and the people in it. But in a moment of stupidity this chance was lost to him.

He did not love Molly, his wife. She was of low birth and could never take her place in his world. But she was pretty when he first met her. He married her because he was kind; he felt sorry for her. It was, of course, Dunstan who suggested it. Dunstan hated Godfrey and enjoyed using his brother's secret against him.

Godfrey's feelings of hate for his wife were growing. 'I can't have these thoughts,' he told himself. 'I'll go to the bar and listen to the talk. It doesn't interest me, but what can I do?'

His dog jumped up. She wanted him to put his hand on her head. But he pushed her away. Without a word or a look he left the room.

Chapter 4   The Thief

Next morning Dunstan Cass started early. On the way to the hunt he rode past Silas Marner's house. The quarry was full of dirty red water. All around it, the earth was very wet. It was an ugly place. Dunstan could hear the noise of the loom. He remembered talk about Silas's money.

'Perhaps Marner could lend Godfrey some money,' he thought. 'Godfrey can pay him back later. He'll have a lot of money one day. Marner knows that. If he doesn't want to lend the money, I can change his mind. He'll be afraid of me. Godfrey can have his hundred pounds and more. Then he can give me some.'

But Dunstan did not stop. He wanted fun and the company of his friends. So he rode on.

When he reached the hunt, he met Bryce. 'Hello!' said Bryce. 'Why are you riding your brother's horse?'

Dunstan smiled and lied easily. 'Wildfire's my horse, now,' he said. 'Godfrey gave me the horse in place of money. I didn't really want him but it helped my brother. I had an offer for him a few days ago – a hundred and fifty pounds. But I shall keep him. He can jump anything – fence, gate or water.'

Bryce knew exactly what Dunstan was trying to do. 'You surprise me,' he said. 'Someone offers you far more than its price and you refuse the offer. That's silly. You'll be lucky if you get a hundred.'

There was more talk. In the end Bryce offered a hundred and twenty pounds. 'You bring Wildfire to Batherley,' he said. 'Then you'll get the money.'

Dunstan accepted the offer but he did not take the horse straight to Batherley. He had a drink with his friends first. Then he said to himself, 'I want to hunt. I don't want to wait in Batherley. There's no danger – I'm always lucky. Wildfire and I will show everyone some excitement.'

At first he enjoyed himself. He was in front, and he jumped the highest fences without trouble. Then he lost his way. Because he was angry, he took the next jump in a hurry. The horse fell and he fell with it. He was unhurt but Wildfire died.

He thought only of himself and not of the horse. He did not want his friends to laugh at him. But nobody saw his fall. He had a drink from a bottle in his pocket and walked towards the nearest trees. Nobody could see him there and he could reach Batherley that way. At Batherley he could borrow a horse and ride home.

No thought of his brother or Wildfire troubled him. The idea of Marner's money interested him even more than before. He decided to walk home. He did not want to go to Batherley and answer questions about the horse. Evening was coming on. In the dark a road was easier than a wood, and the road was quite close. He remembered seeing it a little before the accident. He remembered the post with "Raveloe" on it.

It was strange without a horse but he was holding a riding stick. It really belonged to Godfrey and was borrowed without permission. He liked the feel of it and hit it once or twice against his boots.

He walked a long way and it grew dark. At last he saw a light. 'The quarry is probably not very far away,' he thought. 'Perhaps that's Marner's house. Shall I go and see him now? Godfrey won't ask him for money. He's too weak. But I'll get the money out of the old boy. Fear will do it if there's no other way. Perhaps he'll lend me a light, too.'

In the dark and the rain the road was not very safe. So he turned towards the light. Slowly he felt his way with his riding stick. He fell over two or three times but at last he reached the door. He hit it loudly with his stick.

'That'll put fear in his heart,' he thought, laughing to himself.

The horse fell and he fell with it. He was unhurt but Wildfire died.

But no answer came; nobody moved inside the house. Was the weaver in bed? But the light was burning, and men like Marner did not use lights unnecessarily. Dunstan pushed the door hard. To his great surprise it opened. There was a bright fire inside. He could see every corner of the room – the bed, the loom, the three chairs and the table. Marner was not there.

The fire looked welcoming. Dunsey went in and sat by it. A small piece of meat was cooking there. So the old man didn't live on dry bread, but liked hot meat. It was hanging high up; he didn't want it to cook too quickly. So he was out. But what was he doing outside on a wet night like this? Dunstan remembered his own difficulties on the road. His thoughts continued: 'Perhaps he only wanted to bring in wood for the fire. Perhaps he went too close to the quarry and fell in. I say! That's interesting! If he's dead, who will get his money? It's hidden, of course. Who knows the place? And if anyone takes the money who will know?'

After these exciting questions came one that was even more exciting: 'Where *is* the money?' It drove all clear thought out of his head.

When country people hid their money, there were three favourite hiding places: the roof, the bed, and a hole in the floor. Marner's house had the wrong kind of roof. Quickly, Dunstan went towards the bed. On the way his eyes searched the floor. Sand lay over the stones. It was not thick; he could see the shape of the stones without difficulty – except in one small place. Here the sand covered the stones completely. And the marks of fingers showed in the sand.

Dunstan hurried to the place. With his stick he pushed away the sand and then tested the stones. They moved. Quickly he lifted up two of them. There lay two leather bags. 'How heavy they are!' he thought. 'They're probably full of coins.' He felt round the hole; but there were no more bags. Then he put the stones and the sand back.

All this took little more than five minutes, but to Dunstan it seemed a much longer time. Suddenly he was afraid. He had to get out of the house into the dark. It was safer there. Dunstan picked up the bags and went out. He closed the door quickly behind him.

Outside, the night was darker and the rain was heavier than before.

He was pleased. But it was difficult to find his way, because both his hands were full. 'I mustn't fall,' he thought. 'But there's no need to hurry.' He stepped out into the dark.

Chapter 5   Silas's Pain

When Dunstan Cass left the house, Silas Marner was not far away. An old piece of cloth kept the rain from his back. In his hand was a light. His legs were tired, but his heart held no thought of trouble or change.

Silas was thinking about the hot meal that he was going to have. He liked meat, but he did not buy it himself. This was a present from Miss Priscilla Lammeter, and the Lammeters had only the best food. Other ladies too sometimes gave him presents when he brought their cloth to them.

The evening meal was his favourite. After it he looked at his gold. That night his meal was almost ready when he remembered something. He needed more water for the next day. The weather was bad, and he did not want to leave his warm fire. But he could not spend time collecting water in the morning. He did not want the meat to burn, so he pulled it higher up. Then he took his light and went out. He did not lock the door – the idea never entered his head.

When he returned, his eyes saw no change. He did not see the marks of Dunstan's feet, and soon his own covered them. He moved the meat nearer to the fire. Then he sat down and warmed himself.

The fire lit up his pale face, the weak, tired eyes, and his thin body. He was so different from the people of Raveloe. That perhaps was the reason for their fear and dislike of him. Without the love of God or of friends, Silas had nothing – except his work and his money. The love of gold often drives a man to terrible actions. But poor Silas did not hurt anyone. The gold did not turn him into a bad man. It only kept him from the company of other men.

When he was feeling warm again, he could not wait any longer. He wanted to have the gold on the table during the meal. He got up and put a light on the floor near his loom. Then he pushed away the sand. He picked up the stones. When he saw the empty hole, his heart gave a sudden jump. It couldn't be true. But he felt a terrible fear. His hand started shaking. Quickly he tried the hole again. Perhaps it was the fault of his eyes. Then he held the light in the hole. He was shaking more and more. Finally every part of his body shook, and he dropped the light. He lifted his hands to his head and tried to think. Perhaps he moved his gold the night before, and then forgot? It was not true, and he knew it. But he could not accept the truth; it was too terrible.

He searched in every corner. He turned his bed over and shook each sheet carefully. When he found nothing, he tried the hole again.

He stood up slowly. Perhaps it was a dream. He looked again at the table. He looked behind him and all round the room. He could see all the usual things in it – and the gold was not there.

Again he put his hands on his head, and he gave a loud cry. He walked with great difficulty to his loom, and sat in his usual seat.

'It's gone. A thief has taken my gold,' he said to himself. Then a new thought came to him. 'But one can catch a thief. If I catch this thief, I shall get my gold back.'

He went to the door and opened it. Very heavy rain was falling. Nobody could follow footprints in this weather.

'But when did the thief come?' Silas asked himself. 'When I went out this morning I locked the door. I came back in the light and saw no footprints. And in the evening too there were no signs of a thief. Who in this village is a thief? Jem Rodney never seems very honest. And he takes birds from the Squire's fields and fish from his river. Everyone knows that. I often meet him near my house. He spoke to me about my money once. And another time he made an excuse and came into the house. He stayed a long time. Yes, he's the man. Now I will find him, and get my money back.'

This thought made Silas happier. He was not angry with Jem. He did not want to hurt him. But he wanted his gold back.

Silas knew little about matters of this kind. He thought about it for a few minutes. Finally he said to himself: 'First I should go and tell people the facts. Then the important people in the village – the Rector, the policeman and Squire Cass – will look for the thief. They will soon find who he is. And if Jem Rodney, or some other person, doesn't give back the money, they will make them return it.'

When he had a clear plan, Silas ran out into the rain. He ran all the way to the village. Then, when he was too tired to run, he walked quickly. Soon he was at the village bar.

Chapter 6   At the Village Bar

The villagers looked up from their glasses when Silas arrived at the door of the bar. He did not speak, but looked at them with his strange eyes.

Some of the men were frightened. But Mr Snell, the barman,

When he saw the empty hole, his heart gave a sudden jump.

was not afraid. 'Master Marner!' he cried in a friendly way. 'What is the matter?'

Silas spoke with difficulty. 'A thief!' he said. 'My money! It's gone. I want a policeman – and the Judge – and Squire Cass.'

Silas was very wet and seemed ill. 'Take hold of him, Jem,' the barman ordered. 'He's not well. He'll fall in a moment.'

'Jem Rodney!' Silas turned his strange eyes on the man.

'What do you want?' Jem asked. He was afraid of Silas.

'Did you take my money?' Silas held up his hands. 'Give it to me! Please! I'll – I'll give you a pound.'

'What?' Jem shouted angrily. It almost seemed that he was going to throw his glass at Silas. 'Say that again and you'll be sorry!'

'Let's not have talk like that, Master Marner.' Mr Snell took Silas's arm. 'Calm down and we shall listen to the facts. Now – sit down here.' He took off Silas's wet coat and pushed him into a chair near the fire. 'Now, Master Marner.' He sat down at Silas's side. 'What's all this about a thief?'

Slowly Silas told his story and answered all their questions. His problem was clear to all of them and they began to change their minds about him. He was only a simple man like themselves.

When he finished, Mr Snell put a hand on his arm. 'It's a terrible thing,' he said. 'And we're all sorry for you. But you mustn't talk like that to Jem Rodney, Master Marner. Perhaps he does eat another man's fish from time to time. But he's been here all evening like an honest man.'

Silas suddenly remembered his own trouble long ago and he was sorry. He got up and went to Jem. 'I was wrong,' he said. 'I spoke without thinking. But you were in my house more often than the others. I'm sorry.' His voice sounded tired and sad.

'That's all right, Master Marner,' Jem said.

'How much money was in the bags?' another man asked. His name was Mr Dowlas.

'More than two hundred and seventy-two pounds. I counted it last night.' Silas sat down again in his chair.

'That's not very heavy,' a man said. 'Someone was passing through Raveloe and he took the money. A homeless person, perhaps, who moves from place to place.'

'Why were there no footprints? Why did the stones and sand show no sign of anyone?' Mr Dowlas went on. 'I'll tell you. You can't see very well, Master Marner. Now, I have a plan. You and I and another man will get the policeman. We'll all go to your house and search it. Then, perhaps, we'll find some sign of the thief.'

The barman went to the door and opened it. 'The rain's heavy,' he said.

'I'm not afraid of the rain,' said Mr Dowlas, 'and Judge Malam will be very unhappy if we don't do anything.'

'You're right,' agreed the barman. 'Someone has to go.'

'I'll go with you.' Jem Rodney stood up.

'Good,' said Mr Dowlas. 'Are you ready, Master Marner?'

The barman helped Silas to his feet and gave him an old coat. Silas looked round the room. There was no hope in his brown eyes. The two men were waiting by the door. He put on the coat and followed them into the rain.

Chapter 7   The Hunt for the Thief

Next morning everyone was talking abut the thief. Godfrey joined in the talk and visited the quarry. The ground was wet and showed no clear footprints. But a small tinder-box was lying near the house. Inside it were pieces of stone and metal for making a fire.

It was not Silas's tinder-box. His was standing in its place in his house. 'It was the thief's. He dropped it,' most people said. But

The barman helped Silas to his feet and gave him an old coat.

others did not agree. They could not accept Silas's strange story. 'You'll see,' they said. 'Silas took the money himself. Perhaps he didn't have any. He's half crazy, isn't he?'

At the bar, Squire Cass and the Rector, Mr Crackenthorp, were talking to Mr Snell. Mr Snell was telling the other two about the box.

'When I first heard about the tinder-box,' he said, 'I didn't remember this. About a month ago a pedlar visited Raveloe. The pedlar was thirsty and he came to the bar. He carried a tinder-box like that one. He used it when he smoked. Was the box near Marner's house the pedlar's tinder-box, do you think?'

When they heard about this, the village people took the greatest interest in the pedlar. But Silas could remember nothing about him. 'Yes,' he said to the Squire and the Rector. 'The pedlar came to my door. But he didn't come into the house. I didn't want anything and so he left.' Silas wanted the pedlar to be the thief. He wanted them to search for him. But he could not lie about the man because he was too honest.

People were sorry about Silas's reply. Some were even a little angry. 'Of course it was the pedlar,' they said to each other. 'He didn't go away. He hid and waited. While he was waiting, he dropped the tinder-box by accident. Marner didn't see him because Marner can't see anything. These pedlars are very quick. He only needed one look at Marner's face to see that half-crazy look in it – the look of someone who loves money. Marner's lucky that he wasn't killed. Men like the pedlar often kill for money.'

Godfrey Cass did not agree. He heard the talk about the pedlar in the bar. 'I don't think that it was the pedlar,' he said. 'I bought a knife from the man myself. He had quite a nice smile. He wasn't a bad man at all.'

But Godfrey was not interested in the thief. Dunstan was not at home and his fears were growing. 'Has he had an accident?'

Godfrey thought to himself. 'Perhaps he's sold the horse and is spending the money. He'll come back in a month without anything. I know him so well. Why did I let him have Wildfire?'

He borrowed a horse and rode towards Batherley. There, perhaps, he could hear some news of Dunstan. Suddenly he saw another man on a horse and his heart gave a jump. Was it Dunstan on Wildfire? He rode more quickly.

But it was Bryce. Godfrey did not like the look on his face. Bryce rode up to Godfrey and stopped.

'Your brother's a lucky man, isn't he?' Bryce asked.

'Lucky? Why?'

'Hasn't he come home?'

'No.' Godfrey's fears were growing. 'What's he done with the horse?'

'I offered him a hundred and twenty pounds for it.' Bryce sounded troubled. 'It was a very high price but I've always liked Wildfire. And what did he do? He rode it at a very difficult fence. The horse fell and it was killed. And Dunsey hasn't come home?'

'No.' Godfrey was very angry. 'So he's killed my horse. If he has any sense, he'll stay away.'

'Ah!' Bryce said. 'I wasn't sure. I thought that Dunsey was selling it without permission.'

'He did have my permission,' Godfrey told him.

'I see,' Bryce said. 'Then where is he? Nobody has seen him in Batherley. And the fall didn't hurt him because he walked away.'

'Nothing hurts *him*!' Godfrey said angrily. 'He hurts others.' He looked away from Bryce and his face was troubled. 'I was going to Batherley,' he said. 'But there's no need now. You've told me enough. Are you coming to Raveloe?'

'No, not now,' Bryce answered. 'I've told you about the horse.' He thought for a moment. 'Perhaps Dunsey's afraid of you and is visiting the bar in Whitbridge. He likes the place.'

'Perhaps,' said Godfrey. His heart was heavy. 'He'll be back.'

'I'll leave you, then,' Bryce said. 'I'm very sorry about Wildfire. Goodbye.' He rode away.

Godfrey rode back slowly. Next morning he should tell his father about Dunsey and the money. 'I'll tell him everything,' he thought. 'I'll tell the truth. I'll have to tell him about my wife. I know that Dunsey will come back. If I don't tell the Squire about Molly, Dunsey will. The Squire's a hard man and he'll send me away. I'll lose Nancy and everyone will know about my past.'

He went to sleep late that night. 'At last I've decided,' he thought. 'It won't be easy but it's the right thing to do.'

But in the morning his old fears came back. 'I can't do it,' he thought. 'Everyone will talk about me. And I *can't* lose Nancy. Nothing was clear to me yesterday because I was so angry with Dunstan. I need to stay friendly with him. I need his help, so I'll make excuses for him. Then my father won't be too angry. That's the best plan. If I'm lucky, Dunstan will stay away. Then my secret will be safe. This way everything will be all right.'

Chapter 8   Father and Son

Godfrey had an early breakfast and waited for his father. At last the Squire arrived. He was sixty years old and a big, tall man. He was different from the other Raveloe farmers. He was very sure of himself: his voice and his straight back showed this. Because he met nobody from a higher family than his, he behaved like the most important man in the country.

'What are you waiting for?' he asked his son. Few polite words were exchanged in the Casses' house.

'I wanted to speak to you, sir,' Godfrey said.

'What about?' The Squire started to eat his breakfast.

'It's about Wildfire,' Godfrey told him.

'You've let him fall, have you? Now you want some money

225

for a horse doctor. *My* father wasn't always paying out money to his sons. Too much money is going out and not enough is coming in. People are late with their rents. Fowler promised me a hundred pounds last month but I haven't got it. If he gives me any trouble about the rent, I'll throw him out!'

Godfrey felt even more frightened. But he continued: 'Wildfire isn't hurt, sir; he's dead. Dunsey took him to the hunt a few days ago. I wanted him to sell the horse for me. Bryce offered him a hundred and twenty pounds for Wildfire. But the horse was killed and so I can't pay you the hundred pounds.'

'Pay me?' The Squire was surprised and angry. 'Why? What hundred pounds are you talking about?'

'Fowler did pay his rent, sir,' Godfrey explained. 'He paid me last month when I was at his house. But Dunsey wanted the money and so I gave it to him. I wanted to pay you back before this.'

The Squire's face was red and angry and he spoke with difficulty. 'You gave Dunsey the money? Why? Are you both thieves? Explain yourself. Where is Dunsey? Go and bring him.'

'He hasn't come back, sir.'

'Why not? Did he hurt himself?'

'No, sir. He walked away from the accident. But nobody knows where he is now.'

'If he can't explain, you will!' The angry Squire hit the table. 'Why did you give him the money?'

'I – I don't know, sir.'

'You don't know? Of course you know!' The Squire had a sudden idea. 'I know. You did something terrible and you don't want him to tell me.'

Godfrey was really frightened when he heard this. It was the truth. But he hid his fear and spoke lightly. 'It was only a little thing. A young man's entertainment is not important.'

'Don't talk to me about a young man's entertainment,' the

'I know. You did something terrible and you don't want him to tell me.'

Squire said angrily. 'You're not so young now and I won't accept any more of this. Your way of life has to change. I can't pay for your fun and games any longer. Why can't I enjoy a more comfortable life? Because we never have enough money. How can we have enough money? You don't help me with the work here.'

'I often offer my help, sir,' Godfrey said quietly. 'But you get angry with me. "It's my place and I'll give the orders", you tell me.'

'I don't remember that,' the Squire said. 'But I do remember one thing. Some time ago you wanted to marry Lammeter's daughter. I didn't put difficulties in your way like many fathers. The girl is as good as another. So what's the problem? She hasn't refused you, has she?'

'No,' said Godfrey, feeling very uncomfortable. 'But I think she will.'

'You *think*? Why don't you ask her? You want her, don't you?'

Godfrey looked away. 'Yes,' he said quietly. 'Very much.'

'If you're not man enough, I'll ask Lammeter. He won't refuse *my* family.'

'Please don't do that, sir!' cried Godfrey in great fear. 'Nancy's angry with me at the moment. And I want to speak to her myself. It's a man's duty.'

'Well – do it soon! And live a better life. A wife always asks for that.'

'There are other difficulties, too, sir.' Godfrey was thinking hard before he spoke. 'You don't want to give me one of the farms, do you? Nancy won't want to live in this house with all of us.'

'Won't she?' said the Squire with a hard laugh. 'Ask her. You'll soon see.'

'I need to wait, sir. Please don't say anything to Mr Lammeter in a hurry.'

'If I want to, I shall,' said the Squire. 'I give the orders here. Now I'm going out. Oh! There's another thing. Sell Dunsey's horse and give me the money, will you? He'll keep no more horses at my cost. And when you see him, give him a message. He needn't come back here. He can find work and pay for himself. Now, go and order my horse.'

Godfrey left the room. 'That's the end of that,' he thought. 'Am I pleased or sorry? I don't know. Perhaps I've only brought new trouble on myself. If Father speaks to Mr Lammeter about Nancy, I can't refuse her. What can I do then? I can't marry her. I can't do anything – except wait. Yes, that's it. I'll wait. Perhaps something will change and then the situation will get better.'

Chapter 9   Good Neighbours

Judge Malam was an important man. 'He's cleverer than any of us,' people in Raveloe always said. The Judge thought so too. He listened to the reports about the thief, and the tinder-box interested him greatly. He gave his orders and soon a description of the pedlar was sent to all the villages in the area. But nobody knew the pedlar's name and he was never found.

There was talk in the village, too, when Dunstan Cass did not come back. This was not the first time. Once, after angry words with his father, he left and did not return for six weeks. Dunstan Cass and Silas's gold went missing on the same day. But nobody put these two facts together. Christmas was near; the holiday was in everyone's thoughts. And who could speak against the Casses – the oldest and most important family in Raveloe?

But Christmas brought no end to the pain in Silas's heart. He could only think about one thing. His gold was his only interest in life. Without it he was the saddest of men. His life was empty. The loom was there, of course, and he continued to make cloth.

But where was his money? It was no longer under his feet in the daytime or in his hands at night. Even the thought of his next earnings did not make him feel better. 'What's the use of it?' he thought. 'It will be so little and once I had so much. I'll never have so much again.'

In the evenings he sat alone by his small fire. His head rested on his knees. He cried quietly. He did not want anyone to hear him.

But the village did not forget him. The Rector and the richer families sent him presents of Christmas food. Poorer people greeted Silas in the village. They talked about his trouble and they visited his house. When Silas told them his story they said, 'Well, your money has gone, but there are other poor people around here. And when you can't work, you'll get help. There's money for those who need it.' But they did not make Silas feel better.

One evening Mr Macey visited Silas. He too wanted to help. He sat down in his slow, important way and talked for a time. Then he said, 'Will you listen to me for a minute, Master Marner?'

Silas looked at him with his sad, brown eyes. 'I'll try,' he said.

'Have you got a Sunday suit?'

'No.'

'Buy one. Tookey will make you a suit at a low price. You can pay for it later. Then you can come to church like other people. You should come soon, or it'll be too late. That's what I think.' Mr Macey talked to Silas for a little longer and then he left.

Mrs Winthrop also visited Silas. She was a woman with an honest heart who always did her duty. She finished her housework very early. Then she looked for ways of helping others. Women of this kind are sometimes difficult and unwelcome. But Dolly Winthrop was a kind person. Families always asked for her help in times of trouble. They welcomed her warm heart. She was a pretty woman with a fresh face, but there was something quiet and sad about her.

After his trouble, Silas was often in this good woman's thoughts. One Sunday afternoon she went to see him with her little boy, Aaron. She took some cakes with her. Everyone in Raveloe liked the taste of her cakes.

Silas opened his door without saying a word. Then he moved a chair and made a sign. Dolly sat down. She showed Silas the cakes and said with a smile, 'I made them yesterday, Master Marner. The cakes are specially good. Perhaps you will enjoy some.' She held out the cakes to Silas and he thanked her. Then, in his usual way, he put them close to his weak eyes to look at them. Aaron watched in surprise. He was hiding behind his mother's chair.

'Didn't you hear the church bells this morning, Master Marner?' Dolly asked. 'Perhaps your loom makes too much noise.'

'Yes, I heard them,' Silas replied.

'Well, you poor man,' said Dolly, 'why work on Sunday? Of course you need to cook a hot meal. Everyone has a hot meal on Sundays. But the shop will cook your meat and it only costs two pence. Why don't you come to church on Christmas Day? The church will look beautiful and there'll be music and songs.'

'I don't know anything about the church,' Silas replied.

'Don't you?' Dolly asked. She was rather surprised. She waited for a moment and then went on, 'Well, it's never too late, Master Marner. Come to church and perhaps the result will surprise you. I always feel so happy in church. And if trouble comes, it won't hurt me. That's because I ask for God's help. We all have to do that. If we do our duty, He will not fail us.'

Silas did not agree with Dolly at all but he said nothing. He did not want to go to church. And he never spoke much except about business matters.

231

'The cakes are specially good. Perhaps you will enjoy some.'

By this time, Aaron was less afraid of the weaver. He moved towards him a little. Silas saw him at his mother's side. He offered him a piece of cake. Aaron moved back quickly – then held out his hand.

'What are you thinking, Aaron?' said his mother, but she took him on her knees. 'You don't want cake again, do you? He loves his food,' she continued. 'He's my youngest child, and we can't refuse him anything. His father and I always want him near us.'

She put her hand on Aaron's brown head. 'His pretty face will make Master Marner feel happier,' she thought. But Silas could only see his face with great difficulty.

'And he's got a beautiful voice,' Dolly went on. 'His father's taught him a Christmas song. He learnt very quickly. And that's a good sign because it's a good song. Now, Aaron, stand up and sing the song to Master Marner.'

Aaron made no reply, but put his head on his mother's arm.

'Oh, that's rude,' said Dolly. 'Mother said "Stand up". I'll hold your cake.'

Because his mother was near, Aaron was not too frightened. Also, he wanted to sing to Silas. He was a little afraid of strange Master Marner and he looked at him hard. Then he stood behind the table, so only his head showed. When he began the song, his voice was as clear as a bird's.

Dolly listened happily and looked at Silas. 'He'll want to come to church, now,' she thought.

When Aaron finished, she gave him the cake. 'No other music is as good as Christmas music,' she said. 'And ask yourself this question, Master Marner: "How will it sound in church?" There'll be many more voices in church. It's beautiful. The boy has a pretty voice, hasn't he?'

'Very pretty,' Silas agreed, but he was not really interested. He wanted to show some sign of thanks, though, so he offered Aaron more cake.

'No, thank you,' Dolly said. 'We should go now and I'll say goodbye. But if you're ever ill, I'll come. I'll clean the house and get your food. I'll be pleased to do it. But please don't weave on a Sunday. You'll only have bad thoughts and a sick body.'

Silas thanked Dolly for her kind help. But he was pleased when she left. He could go back to his work.

And he did not listen to her or to Mr Macey. He stayed at home on Christmas Day. He ate his meat with a sad heart. Outside there was ice and a strong wind. In the evening snow fell and the dark closed round him.

But in Raveloe village everyone was enjoying the service. After church they all walked home. They walked quickly because it was so cold. The rest of the day was free, so they could eat, drink and enjoy themselves.

At Squire Cass's family party, nobody spoke Dunstan's name. Nobody was sorry that he was not there. Most of the talk was the same every year. Uncle Kimble, the doctor, told exciting stories about his early life in London. Games of cards followed the stories. Aunt Kimble made her usual mistakes. Uncle Kimble got angry when he was beaten.

But the party on Christmas Day was only a small, quiet one. The real party of the season was on the day before the New Year. In the evening, the Casses always held a great dance. It marked the end of all disagreements from the past year. They invited all their old friends from far and near.

Godfrey Cass thought about this dance with both hope and fear. 'Next year, Dunsey may come back and tell my father about my wife,' he thought. 'Perhaps my father will learn the secret some other way. But at the dance I'll see Nancy again. I can talk to her and dance with her.' There was some hope in that thought.

Chapter 10   A New Year in Raveloe

Everyone enjoyed the party. There were a lot of good things to eat and drink. Old friends met again; people made new friends. There was dancing, music and happy talk. And Godfrey's dreams came true. He found himself alone with Nancy.

He danced with her until the Squire accidentally stepped on her long dress. Priscilla, Nancy's sister, promised to repair the dress. So Godfrey took Nancy to a small room away from the dancing and they waited there for Priscilla.

'You needn't stay,' Nancy told Godfrey coldly. 'I'll be all right.'

'But I want to stay,' Godfrey said.

'You'll miss the next dance,' Nancy said.

'That doesn't matter. I want to be with you. That's more important than anything.'

'You surprise me!'

'Can't you forgive me, Nancy?' Godfrey took a step towards her. 'I often behave badly but I want to change.'

'Change is a good thing.' Nancy's voice was a little softer. 'But it's always better if no change is necessary.'

'You've got a hard heart, Nancy. I want to be better but you don't help me. I'm unhappy and it doesn't matter to you.'

'How can you talk about hard hearts? Who behaved badly first? How much do I matter to *you*?'

Nancy's angry words pleased Godfrey. Perhaps she loved him even now. But at that moment Priscilla hurried in. 'Do I have to go?' he asked.

'Please yourself,' said Nancy. She looked down at her dress.

'I'll stay,' said Godfrey. 'Tomorrow is not important,' he thought. 'I'll enjoy tonight.'

In Nancy's company, Godfrey Cass forgot his wife. But Godfrey was the only person in his wife's mind. She was walking slowly through the snow on the Raveloe road. Her child was in her arms.

She was remembering an angry speech of Godfrey's: 'I will never take you to Raveloe. I don't want my family or my friends to meet you. I will die first.' Molly never forgave him for those words. She knew about the great New Year party, and she had a plan.

'So he'll leave me here, will he?' she said to herself. 'He'll hide me away, and enjoy himself with his fine friends. But I'll put an end to his enjoyment. I'll show the Squire his oldest son's wife. They can all see my dirty clothes. They can all see my tired face – and I was pretty once. They can all see my little child. They will see that it has its father's hair and eyes.'

Godfrey sent money to Molly, and she had enough for good clothes. She knew this. But she spent all her money on opium, and she hated her husband. When she took it she forgot her troubles; she forgot everything except her child. Opium is a terrible thing. At first you enjoy it, but soon you cannot live without it. In the end it destroys you. It was destroying Molly. She loved her child, but she did not always remember to feed it.

It was seven o'clock and she was not very far from Raveloe. But she did not know this. There was no sign of any end to the road. She needed help, but she had no friend except opium. She wanted to feed the child in her arms, but she was tired and ill. She took a piece of opium from her pocket and ate it.

She walked on with more and more difficulty. The wind was like ice, but now she did not feel it. She forgot her plan, her duty to her child, everything. She just wanted to sleep. She left the road and lay down under a small tree. The snow was soft. Her arms were holding the child and it did not wake.

But when deep sleep came, the mother's arms and fingers opened. The little head fell back, and the blue eyes looked up. The child gave a little cry; it missed its mother's arms. But she

'Can't you forgive me, Nancy?'

heard nothing. Suddenly the child forgot her mother, forgot the cold snow. A light was moving across the white ground. It came towards the child, but never reached her. She felt that she had to catch the beautiful light. On hands and knees she moved towards it. She couldn't catch it in the snow. She lifted her head; the light was coming from a place not far away. The little one got up and walked through the snow. An old, dirty piece of cloth covered her dress. Part of it hung down behind and moved across the ground.

The little one continued walking until she came to Silas's open door.

The light came from his fire. She sat down in front of it and warmed her hands. She did not miss her mother because she often played alone. At first she made happy little noises to the fire. But soon all of her was warm. The little golden head touched the floor and the blue eyes closed.

But where was Silas? Earlier in the day someone told him to sit up and listen to the church bells. 'If you hear them at New Year, perhaps they'll bring you luck. Perhaps your money will come back.' So Silas was outside listening to the bells.

While he was outside he suddenly felt ill and weak. For a time he saw nothing and heard nothing. When the feeling left him, he went back inside. He closed the door, returned to the fire and sat down. Suddenly, in the fire's weak light, he saw something gold on the floor. Was it – surely not – his own gold? His heart beat faster and faster and he could not move.

At last he put out his hand. But his fingers did not feel the usual hard shape of coins. They touched soft, warm hair. Silas fell on his knees in surprise. He put his head down and saw the child asleep. All over its head was hair the colour of gold.

'Is this my little sister?' was Silas's first thought. 'Has she come back in a dream? I carried her in my arms when she was small. But she died when I was a little boy. *Is* this a dream?'

He pushed the sticks in the fire together, and threw on new

ones. Soon the fire was giving more light. The child was there on the floor. The little round shape and the old clothes were clear to his eyes. She was very like his sister.

'How did she get in, and why didn't I see her?' he thought to himself. He could not answer the question, and thought made him tired. He sat back in his chair and closed his eyes. He remembered his sister and his old home, the old streets and Lantern Yard.

Suddenly there was a cry. The child was awake and wanted her mother. Silas lifted her on his knees. She hung round his neck and gave louder cries. Silas held her tight and made calming sounds.

He was very busy in the next hour. He warmed some of his own food. He found some brown sugar and added that. Then he fed the child with a spoon. Her cries stopped and her blue eyes opened wide. After a time she got off his knee. She took a few steps, but she could not stand up very well. Silas jumped up and followed her. He did not want her to fall and hurt herself. But she only sat back on the floor and pulled at her shoes. Her little face had an angry look. Silas took her on his knee again. He knew nothing about the troubles of small children. But at last he understood. The tight wet shoes were hurting her warm feet. With difficulty he took the shoes off. The little one looked at her toes and laughed. They were a joke and a mystery. She showed them to Silas.

He was holding the wet shoes. 'She came in from the snow,' he suddenly thought. He lifted up the child. He carried her to the door and opened it. Then she remembered her mother again, and cried out for her. He put his head down to look at the ground. With difficulty he saw her little footprints in the snow. He followed them into the trees. She held out her hands and tried to jump out of his arms. She was crying again and again for her mother. At last he saw a shape. He knew without a second

Silas held her tight and made calming sounds.

look that it was a body. The head was under a tree, resting on the ground. It was almost covered in snow.

Chapter 11   The End of a Marriage

At the Squire's house, the guests were talking and dancing happily. The Squire was at the centre of a group of friends. He was laughing and telling them a joke. Godfrey stood against the wall. He was watching Nancy and hoping for another dance with her. For a moment he turned his eyes away and looked towards the door.

A sudden cold fear entered his heart. He saw Silas and he saw his own child in Marner's arms. 'No!' he said softly. But there was no mistake. The child with the golden hair was his.

Other people's eyes began to fall on Silas. The Rector and Mr Lammeter hurried across to him. Godfrey followed them slowly. His face was white.

'Marner!' the Squire called. 'What are you doing here? What do you want?' The room grew quiet.

'I need the doctor,' Silas said.

'What's wrong?' asked the Rector.

'It's a woman,' Silas told him. 'She's in the snow near my door. She's dead – or almost dead.'

'Don't talk about it here,' said the Rector. 'Think of the ladies. We don't want to worry them. Go into that room there. I'll bring Doctor Kimble to you.'

But by this time there was a crowd of ladies around Silas. They showed great interest in the pretty child. She was half afraid of so many people and all the lights. But they excited her, too. Sometimes she smiled and sometimes she hid her face.

'Whose child is it?' Nancy asked Godfrey. She was standing next to him now. He turned and looked at her. For a moment he

He saw Silas and he saw his own child in Marner's arms.

could not speak. Then he said, 'I don't know. He found a woman in the snow. He says the child's hers.'

'Why don't you leave the poor child here, Master Marner?' suggested kind Mrs Kimble. She looked at the child's dirty clothes. 'Someone will look after her.'

'No – no – I can't leave her!' Silas held the child more tightly. 'She's come to me and I'll look after her.'

Doctor Kimble came in from the card room. He spoke to the Squire and then hurried out. Godfrey followed him. 'Get me a pair of thick shoes, Godfrey, will you?' Doctor Kimble asked. 'And someone should run and find Dolly Winthrop. She's the best person for this kind of situation.' He hurried away with Silas.

'I'll go,' Godfrey said quickly. 'I'll bring Mrs Winthrop.' Godfrey hurried away, too. He collected his hat and coat. But he forgot he was wearing his dancing shoes.

In a few minutes he and Dolly were walking quickly towards the quarry. 'You go back, sir,' she said. 'You'll get wet feet and then you'll be ill.'

'No, I'll wait here,' said Godfrey. They were outside Marner's house. 'Tell me if I can do anything.'

'Yes, sir,' said Dolly and went into the house.

Godfrey did not really hear her. He did not think about his wet feet or the icy cold. He had only one thought. 'Is Molly dead?' he asked himself again and again. 'Can I marry Nancy now? Then I don't need to have any more secrets. There's the child, of course. I'll look after her. I'll find a way. But perhaps Molly will live. If she does, I'll have no chance of a happy life.'

Godfrey waited, without any idea of the time. At last Uncle Kimble came out. Godfrey hid his thoughts, and walked towards him.

'I was here, so I waited,' he said.

'There was no need. Why didn't you send one of the men? I can't do anything: she's quite dead.'

Godfrey's heart beat fast. 'What kind of woman is she?' he asked.

'She's a young woman, but very thin. Her hair is long and black. She had no money, and she needed new clothes. But she was wearing a wedding ring. They'll take her away tomorrow. I'm going back now. Come along.'

'I want to look at her,' said Godfrey. 'I saw a woman like that yesterday. I'll join you later.'

He went in. His wife lay there. He hated her while she lived. But now she was dead. He took only one look at her. Sixteen years later, when he told the full story of this night, he remembered every line on her sad, tired face.

He turned to the fire. Silas was sitting there with the child in his arms. She was quiet but not asleep. Her wide blue eyes looked up at Godfrey, but gave no sign. He was half pleased and half sorry when she did not know him. The blue eyes turned away from him slowly. They looked back to the weaver's strange face. A small hand gave a soft pull at Silas's ear.

'You'll take the child to the children's home tomorrow?' Godfrey's voice did not show his interest.

'Who says that?' said Silas quickly. 'Do I have to take her?'

'You don't want to keep her, do you? You're old and unmarried.'

'Nobody will take her away from me, except her family. And there's no sign of a family. The mother's dead, and the child clearly has no father. She's alone – and I'm alone.'

'Poor little child!' said Godfrey. 'She needs new clothes. Please take this.'

He pushed a gold coin into Silas's hand. Then he hurried away after Doctor Kimble.

'I don't know that woman,' he told him. 'I thought I did. The child's pretty, isn't she? Marner wants to keep her.'

'I can understand that,' the doctor said. 'I wanted a child

myself once. But let's hurry back to the dance. Your feet are wet, and I'm cold.'

They walked on without speaking. 'I hated Molly but I'm sad that she's dead,' he thought. 'Nobody will know my secret, now. Dunsey will want to talk, if he comes back. But I can give him money and he'll keep quiet.' He could marry Nancy without fear and his future seemed happier. 'I won't tell Nancy about Molly,' he said to himself. 'It will only make us both unhappy. There's my child, of course. But Marner will keep her. She'll stay in the village. I'll give her what she needs. Nobody will know. She'll be happy enough.'

Chapter 12   A Child's Love

Soon everyone in the village was talking about Silas again. 'He's keeping that child,' they said. 'It's a crazy idea. But he's a rather kind old man, after all.' The women were most pleased. Different mothers gave him different instructions about looking after the child. But they were all worried about the time that a two-year-old child needs. 'He's quite alone and he has to work. How can he do it?' they asked themselves.

Silas liked Dolly Winthrop best of all the women. He showed her Godfrey's money and asked her about clothes.

'Oh, Master Marner, don't you buy clothes, except a pair of shoes. I've got Aaron's baby clothes. She can have those. She'll grow so fast and she doesn't really need new things. Aaron's are fine.'

While Dolly found the clothes, Silas heated water. Then Dolly held the child on her knees and washed her. The child laughed and held her toes. Sometimes she made baby noises and called for her mother. But she was not unhappy. Even when her mother was with her, she did not often answer her daughter.

Dolly kissed the clean, golden hair. 'She's prettier than a flower!' she cried. 'And the poor mother died from the cold! How sad for the child. But God looked after her. Your door was open and she walked in like a hungry little bird. You were right to keep her, Master Marner. After all, she came to you specially. Not everyone agrees but that's what I say. She'll give you some trouble, while she's so small. But I'll come and look after her. I get up early so I've got a lot of time. I'll be happy to come at about ten o'clock.'

'Thank you – you're very kind,' Silas said. 'But I also want to do things for her myself. I want her to like me. I can learn.'

'Of course you can,' said Dolly kindly. 'Some men know exactly what to do with children.' Dolly picked up a little shirt. 'You see this,' she continued. 'You put this on first.'

'Yes,' said Silas. He watched closely. His face was close to the child's and she put her arms round his neck. She made baby noises and kissed him.

'You see!' Dolly said. 'She likes you best. She wants to sit on your knee. Take her and put her things on yourself.'

Silas took the child and her touch woke strange and exciting feelings in him. He took the clothes from Dolly and put them on the child. Dolly told him what to do. The child laughed and played.

'That's good,' Dolly said. 'It's not so difficult, is it?' She watched him for a moment and then asked: 'What will you do with her when you're working? She's a dear little thing but she'll be more trouble every day. She can't reach the fire, but she'll break things. If she can cut herself, she will. I know children.'

Silas thought hard. 'I'll tie her to my loom,' he said. 'I'll tie her with a long piece of cloth.'

'Perhaps that will work. I'll bring her a few toys and she can sit and play with them. I'm sometimes almost sorry that all my children are boys. Girls like to help in the house and wash and

246

make clothes. I can't teach my boys those things. But perhaps one day I can teach this little one.'

'But she'll belong to me,' said Silas quickly.

'Of course she'll be yours, if you do the right thing,' Dolly agreed. 'But you have to be a good father to her. You should take her to church so she can learn with the other children. Then, if she wants God's help, she'll know the right words. My Aaron can say them; the Rector himself can't say them better.'

Dolly's words troubled Silas. He did not like her talk of God, so he did not answer.

'And there's another thing,' she went on. 'You need to choose a name for the child. What shall we call her?'

'My sister's name was Eppie,' Silas said. 'It's short for Hephzibah.'

'Oh, I like Eppie much better. It's easier and shorter. And so I'll go now, Master Marner. Don't worry about the dirty clothes. I'll wash them. Ah, isn't she pretty? I'll bring my Aaron and he can show her his toys.'

So, one day, a very clean Silas took Eppie to church. The Rector gave Eppie her new name and welcomed her to the church. Everything was strange to Silas. But he remembered Dolly's words about the child and her need for the church. So he took Eppie there every Sunday and met more people that way.

He had a new interest in his life now. When he had gold, he only wanted to live alone. He could not forget the past. Eppie turned his thoughts to new things and to the future. He took an interest in other families, and thought, 'She too will understand a father's love one day.'

In the past, he worked all the time to earn his gold. His eyes saw nothing except the cloth that he was weaving. His ears heard nothing except the noise of his loom. Now Eppie called him away from work. She made every day a holiday. Her fresh young life woke something in his own heart. He saw the signs of spring.

And because she was happy, he was happy too.

When summer came, Silas and Eppie enjoyed themselves together. Every day he carried her past the quarry. He sat on a favourite bank and she played. The field was thick with flowers. She picked some and brought them to Silas. Then she listened to the birds. She taught him a game. A bird called; he held up his hand and they both waited. It called again, and he dropped his hand. This was a fine joke, and she laughed and laughed.

Soon she could talk a little and she was always asking questions. Her eyes missed nothing. Then, when she was three years old, there was another problem. She started behaving badly like other small children. She did not listen when Silas told her things. This gave him a lot of trouble.

'Just hit her softly, Master Marner,' said Dolly. 'A child needs that sometimes. Or there's another way. You burn wood on your fire. Then put her – just once – in the cupboard where you keep the wood. I did that to Aaron. He's my youngest, and I never wanted to hit him. I took him out after a minute, but that was enough. He was dirty and frightened. I washed him and changed his clothes – and it was as good as hitting him. But you'll have to choose one or other, Master Marner. It's your duty. Either you hit her softly, or you put her in the cupboard. If you don't, she'll never learn to behave.'

Silas was sad. 'She's right,' he thought, 'But I *can't* do it. I can't hurt Eppie. I can't even shake her. If I'm angry with her, perhaps she will love me less.'

As a result of Silas's fear, Eppie saw the chance for more exciting adventures. One day Silas was starting a new piece of work. He was using a pair of scissors to cut cotton. He usually kept them away from the child, and the sound of the scissors interested her. She watched when he used them. She made plans.

When he no longer needed the scissors, Silas sat down. The noise of the loom began. Eppie was sitting on her little bed. She

So, one day, a very clean Silas took Eppie to church.

could not go very far because she was tied to the loom with a piece of cloth. But the scissors were not in their usual place. She could reach them.

Very quickly she left her place and took the scissors. She went back to the bed, and turned her back. With little difficulty she cut the piece of cloth. The door was open. In a moment she ran out in the sun. Poor Silas saw nothing. He only thought: 'How good she is being! How quiet!'

A little later he needed the scissors. Then he saw that Eppie was not in the room. Frightened, he ran out and called her name. His eyes turned towards the red water of the quarry. He was as cold as ice, and his body was shaking. When did she leave the house?

There was one chance: perhaps she was in one of the fields. She knew the way. The grass was high, and poor Silas searched one field with no result. He went across to the next field. Here there was a big pool. In winter it was full of water. In summer it was half empty and the sides were soft earth. By its side sat Eppie.

Near her was the deep footprint of an animal. She was using her shoe to fill it with water. She was talking to the shoe in a happy voice. The foot without the shoe was on the wet earth. A young cow was watching her with surprise and fear.

Eppie needed a lesson; that was clear. But Silas could not hit her. He was too happy that she was safe. He picked her up and covered her face with kisses. At the same time he was almost crying.

But when he reached home again, he remembered Dolly's words. 'Perhaps she'll run away again,' he thought. 'And she won't be so lucky a second time. There are so many dangers around. I've got to do something. I don't want to, but I'll put her in the cupboard with the wood.'

The child was on his knees. Suddenly he showed her her dirty feet and clothes, and said: 'Bad Eppie! Eppie is a very bad girl.

With little difficulty she cut the piece of cloth.

Eppie took the scissors and cut with them. Then she ran away. Bad girls go into the dark cupboard. Eppie is going to go into the cupboard.'

He waited. 'Perhaps she'll cry and that'll be enough,' he thought. But the idea of a new place excited Eppie. She looked pleased and began to climb off his knees. There was no other way. He had to do his duty. He was afraid, but he put her into the cupboard. Then he closed the door. After a moment a little cry came out: 'Open, open!' Silas opened the door. 'Now Eppie will never be bad again,' he said. 'Or she will go into the cupboard – a black bad place.'

Silas did not do much work that morning. 'But I've done the right thing,' he thought. 'She won't give any more trouble now. But why didn't she cry more?'

In half an hour she was clean again, and she was wearing clean clothes. He turned away from her and saw the long piece of cloth. 'I'll have to mend that,' he said to himself. 'But there's no hurry. She won't give any more trouble now. I'll put her in her little chair near the loom.'

When he next turned round, her face and hands were dirty again. She was looking at him from the cupboard with a sweet smile. 'Eppie's in the cupboard!' she said.

'It's no good,' Silas told Dolly later. 'It's only fun to her. And it'll always be the same if I don't hurt her. And I can't do that. If she makes a bit of trouble, I'll live with it. It won't last.'

So Eppie received only love and smiles from Silas. In the outside world it was the same. She usually went with him to even the furthest farms. He carried her and his heavy bag of cloth. It was not easy, but he did not want to leave her with Dolly. Everyone in these farms and in the village showed great interest in the weaver's child. And they liked him more. In the old days they were afraid of him. Sometimes they gave him presents, it is true. But that was because he was the only weaver in the area.

Now he was one of them; he had a child. They met him with smiles. They invited him into their houses. They asked all the usual questions about young children. Some joked with him: 'You chose a difficult job, Master Marner. Most men leave the little ones to the women. But you weavers have quicker hands than ours, and you understand women's work.'

The older men and women explained all the possible difficulties and dangers. They felt Eppie's round arms and legs. 'Yes, she is well now,' they said. 'But there are so many possible problems. Perhaps you'll be lucky. It'll be a fine thing if she can help you later. Because you'll be old, Master Marner, and you'll need help.'

People often carried Eppie around their farms. Sometimes they showed her the young animals; sometimes they picked fruit from the trees. Other children welcomed her, too. And they did not fear Silas when she was near him. He and she were like one person; there was love between them. And there was love between the child and all the world. Everybody and everything loved her. So nobody, young or old, feared or hated Silas any more.

PART TWO

Chapter 13   A Quiet Life

Sixteen years later, it is a bright autumn Sunday in Raveloe. The villagers are leaving the church after the service. We know a few of them.

That tall, fair man of forty is not very different from the young Godfrey Cass. The old Squire is dead now, so Godfrey is the new Squire Cass. His eyes are shining and there are no lines on his face. Perhaps his pretty wife is looking a bit older. But Time has not been too hard to Nancy. She has met the tests of life. Her strong, kind mouth and clear, honest eyes show this. And who is leaving the church after them? Silas Marner's large, brown eyes see further now and he has more interest in the world around him. But he is fifty-five and the shape of his back and his white hair make him look like an old man. Next to him walks a beautiful girl of eighteen.

A fine young man in a new suit walks behind her. She is the one subject of his thoughts and she knows this. But she hides her thoughts and talks to her father.

'That's a pretty tree, Father,' Eppie said. 'Perhaps we can have a garden. But you can't dig it and I don't want you to. It's hard work.'

'Yes, I can,' said Silas. 'The evenings are long and I can do a bit then.'

The path was wider here and the young man came to Eppie's side.

'I can dig it for you, Master Marner,' he said. 'I shall enjoy doing it after work.'

'Hello, Aaron,' Silas smiled. 'I didn't see you. If you can help

Next to him walks a beautiful girl of eighteen.

me, we'll soon have a garden.'

'I'll come to the quarry this afternoon,' Aaron told him. 'We can talk about the size of the garden then.'

'You see, Father?' Eppie said. 'You needn't do any hard work. We'll put the plants in after Aaron digs the ground.'

'That's right,' Aaron said. 'I can bring you some plants.'

'Thank you,' Silas said. 'You're like your mother, you're very kind.'

'Oh, no,' said Aaron. 'I'm happy to do it. You'll soon have a fine garden. But I should get home now or Mother will miss me. I'll see you this afternoon.' He turned back towards the village and Eppie and Silas went on up the quiet path.

'Oh, Father!' Eppie held Silas's arm tight and kissed him. 'I'm so pleased. I'll really enjoy a little garden.'

'Will you?' said Silas with a quiet smile. 'It'll be a lot of trouble for Aaron.'

Eppie laughed. 'No, it won't,' she said. 'He'll enjoy it.'

When they were near the house, a brown dog ran out. It danced round them. Inside, a cat sat in the sun by the window.

This happy animal life was one new thing about the house, and there were other changes too. Everything was clean and light and showed signs of Dolly Winthrop's help. The fine table and chairs, beds and other furniture came from the old Squire's house. Mr Godfrey Cass was very kind to the weaver. Everyone agreed about that.

Silas sat down and watched Eppie. She covered the table with a clean cloth and took the hot food from the fireplace. Silas loved his stone fireplace. It was a true friend like the old brown pot. Most important of all, it was where he found Eppie.

He ate quietly and soon put down his knife and fork. He watched Eppie. The cat was climbing up her arm and she was laughing. Her golden hair and white neck shone against the dark blue colour of her dress. The dog and the cat were on each side of her. She held up a piece of food and they both wanted it. Then she broke it in two and gave a piece to each of them.

'If you're ready, Father,' Eppie said, 'go outside. It's a beautiful day. Sit in the sun and smoke.'

Outside, many thoughts filled his head. Years ago he was a very unhappy man. Now he accepted the Raveloe way of life and the village people accepted him. He thought about William Dane and Lantern Yard. He was happy there too. He remembered talking to Dolly about that time and asking her about it. 'Why did that dark shadow cover the best years of my life?' he asked her.

'I don't know,' Dolly told him. 'You no longer believed in God. Perhaps if a man doesn't believe in God, he can't be happy. Without God he is without any other friends. A man has to believe and to help other people.'

'But I couldn't believe when I left Lantern Yard,' he told her. 'It was too difficult.'

'Of course it was,' Dolly agreed. 'I can talk, but I wasn't in your situation. I'm sorry.'

'No, no,' said Silas. 'You're right. There's good in this world. I can feel it now. But we don't always see it. A lot of good is hidden behind our problems and the bad times. William Dane hurt me badly but then the child came to my house. Things like that are not accidents.'

This discussion took place when Eppie was quite small. Now she was becoming a woman. Because their love was complete, Silas always told her everything. No other way was possible, in any case. Village people are always talking, Silas knew that someone was going to tell her one day. So she knew about her mother's death in the snow; she also knew that Silas was not her father.

When she grew older, Silas gave her her mother's ring. Her thoughts were with her mother and she did not ask about her real father. She knew the happiness of a mother's love; Mrs Winthrop was an excellent example. Again and again she asked Silas questions about her mother. What kind of a person was she? What did she look like? How did he find her under the tree?

On this afternoon Eppie looked at the little tree when she came out of the house. 'Father,' she said. Her voice was soft and sad. 'Let's move the tree to the garden. It can go in a corner and I'll put flowers round it.'

'We won't forget the tree,' Silas promised. 'But we need a wall round the garden. If we don't have one, animals will come in. They'll damage the plants.'

'There are a lot of stones,' Eppie said. 'We'll use those. Look there! They're all round the quarry.' She walked to the quarry to show him and then gave a little cry of surprise. 'Father! Come and look. The water's gone down. Yesterday the quarry was quite full.'

Silas came to her side and explained. 'They were working on Mr Cass's fields around here. Someone said that these fields hold too much water. So they cut narrow paths across the fields and now the water can run away. Our land will be drier, too.'

'Oh! It's too heavy!' Eppie tried to carry a stone but dropped it.

'Come and sit down,' Silas told her. 'You need someone's help – and my arms aren't strong enough now.'

They sat quietly together and Eppie held her father's hand. Shadows from a tree danced round them.

'Father,' Eppie said at last. 'If I marry, shall I wear my mother's wedding ring?'

Silas turned to look at her. 'Does Aaron want to marry you?'

'Yes. He's almost twenty-four and he's got a lot of work.'

'Will you accept him?'

'I think so. But I shan't leave you. Aaron wants us all to live together. He says that he'll be as good as a son to you.'

'Aren't you too young?'

'Father! Come and look. The water's gone down.'

'I don't know. I'm very happy with you. I don't want any change.'

Silas thought for a moment and then he said, 'Things will change, Eppie. I'll get older and need more help. I know that you'll be happy to help me. But it's not right. I want you to have a husband. Someone young and strong – someone who will look after you until the end of your life.' He thought again. 'I like Aaron,' he said. 'I like him very much. I know that you do, too. We'll ask Mrs Winthrop. She always knows what's best.'

'Look!' said Eppie. Dolly and Aaron were coming along the path to Silas's house. 'There they are.'

'We'll go and meet them.' Silas stood up and helped Eppie to her feet.

Chapter 14   Trouble in Raveloe

On that same afternoon, Nancy Cass was sitting alone. Godfrey was out. 'I'm going to the fields by the quarry,' her husband told her before he left. 'I want to look at the work there. The fields will probably be dry now. I'll be back at teatime.'

Nancy thought about Godfrey. He was quiet and kind but there was often a sad look in his eyes. 'Is it because we haven't any children?' she asked herself. 'A woman can spend all her time looking after her husband. But a man wants to plan for his family. A man needs a wife and children as well. Godfrey wanted to adopt a child. Was I wrong to refuse?'

Nancy did not think that the adoption of other people's children was a good idea. She and Godfrey talked about it many times after the early death of Nancy's baby. They were both very sad about the death. 'We should adopt a child,' Godfrey said at that time. 'It will make our lives happier.'

But Nancy did not want an adopted child. The years went by

and they were unable to have more children. But she continued to refuse. 'It is not right,' she said. 'Don't you remember that lady in Royston? She adopted a child and it behaved very badly. I can't agree, dear. If we have no children, that's hard. But it's for God to decide.'

'Why should a child bring trouble on us?' Godfrey said. 'Marner adopted a child. They're happier together than most people. But he's a poor man. It's difficult for him to look after the girl. We can adopt Eppie.'

Godfrey never told Nancy about his first wife, Molly. He was sad that they had no children. But most of all he wanted Eppie, his own child, and he could not explain the reason to Nancy. He did not think about Silas. Silas loved Eppie more than life itself, but Godfrey did not understand this. 'Marner will want the best for Eppie,' he thought. 'He needn't trouble about money any more. It's a problem for him and I can solve it.'

But Nancy did not agree to this either. 'God decides these matters, dear,' she told him. 'He knows better than we do. If we adopt a child, we'll be sorry.'

So Godfrey did not talk about Eppie again. He understood his wife's feelings. In some matters she was the stronger person. Sometimes, because of this, he was rather afraid of her.

'I can never tell her about my first wife,' he thought. 'If I do, perhaps she'll hate the child. I didn't tell her my secret when I first married her. I can't tell her now; I don't want to destroy our love.'

And so Nancy was thinking about Godfrey. 'Was I wrong?' she asked herself. 'Old people feel the need for children. If I die, Godfrey will be all alone. But I can't look into the future. I'll just do my best now.'

A girl came in with the tea. Nancy looked at her and asked, 'Has the master come back, Jane?'

'No,' Jane said. She was excited about something. 'Can you see

261

all the people? They're hurrying past the front window. Perhaps there's been an accident.'

'Oh, it won't be anything bad,' said Nancy. 'Perhaps one of Mr Snell's animals has got out again.'

'Even farm animals sometimes attack people,' said Jane. She was frightened but she was enjoying her fear.

When Jane left, Nancy got up. She went to the front window. 'That girl is always putting fears into my head,' she said to herself. 'When *will* Godfrey come?' She could see nothing along the road. 'I'm worrying like a child,' she thought. 'There's no sign of trouble. Why am I afraid? Godfrey won't return this way; he'll come across the fields.'

But she continued to stand there. She looked at the church and the trees in the Rector's garden. The beautiful view did not take away her fear. It grew. A shadow is darker on a bright day.

Chapter 15   Secrets

Godfrey opened the door. Nancy turned from the window with happy eyes. 'Dear, you've come at last! I'm so happy. I–'

She stopped suddenly. Godfrey was putting down his hat. His hand was shaking and his face was white. He sat down like an old man and said quietly, 'Please sit down, my dear. I've got some terrible news.'

'It isn't – Father?' Nancy asked. Her voice shook as she sat down.

'No,' Godfrey said. 'It's Dunstan. He left 16 years ago and he never returned. Now they've found his body. There isn't much of it.' He put his hand to his head. Nancy waited and then he went on: 'The quarry is dry now. The water has gone after our work in the fields. He's down there. There's his watch and his ring. And there's my riding stick with the gold top. After sixteen years, there

Nancy turned from the window with happy eyes.

he lies between two great stones.'

Godfrey stopped again.

'What's wrong?' Nancy cried. 'Is there something worse to tell? Did he kill himself?'

'No, he didn't kill himself,' Godfrey said quietly. 'But there is something worse. He was the thief. Dunstan took Silas Marner's gold.'

'Oh, Godfrey!' Nancy cried. She felt very sorry for her husband. He did not move or look at her. She waited. 'He hasn't finished,' she thought. 'There is more to tell.'

At last he continued: 'There are no secrets in the end, Nancy. I've got a secret that I won't hide from you any longer. I don't want others to tell you and I don't want to die first. So I'll tell you now.'

Nancy looked at him in fear. Their eyes met. Each was like a stranger to the other.

'When I married you, I behaved very badly,' he told her. 'I hid something from you. You remember Eppie's mother? Marner found her dead in the snow outside his house. That woman was my wife. Eppie is my child.'

Nancy looked quickly away from him. 'You'll never feel the same about me again,' Godfrey said and his voice shook a little. Nancy did not answer.

'I hid it all from you,' he went on sadly. 'I failed in my duty to the child. But I loved you so much and I didn't want you to refuse me. I did not love my first wife. She was a bad woman. It was a terrible time.'

He waited in great fear. Finally Nancy lifted her eyes to his and spoke. Her voice was not angry – only very sad.

'Why didn't you tell me this when you first wanted Eppie here? I refused because I didn't know everything. I could never refuse *your* child.' She began to cry. 'Oh, Godfrey, why didn't you bring her to our house from the first? We had the chance of a happy life together. When my little baby died, I–' She could say no more.

'I couldn't tell you. I wanted your love. Could you love me in those days with a child?' he asked.

'I can't tell. I never wanted to marry another man. But you were wrong to hide all this. It's wrong to live a lie.'

'Can you ever forgive me?' he asked.

'You haven't hurt me, Godfrey. You're a good husband to me. But you should do the right thing for Eppie.'

'We can take her now. I shan't hide things any more.'

'It'll be different,' said Nancy in a sad voice. 'She's no longer a child. But you should accept her as yours and bring her here to live with us. I'll do my duty to her too. Perhaps with God's help she will love me.'

Chapter 16   Father and Daughter

Silas and Eppie were sitting together at home. On the table near them lay the gold.

'I counted it every night,' Silas said. 'When it was stolen, my life was completely empty. And I wanted to have it back and feel it again. Then you came. What your old father felt for you! You didn't know then, Eppie, when you were small.'

'But I know now.' Eppie took his hand. 'You saved me from a life in a children's home. A child gets no love there.'

'My dear, you saved me from a future that was far worse. My troubles almost killed me. The money was stolen at the right time. Now it's back again at the right time because you'll need it for your marriage.'

At that moment they heard visitors outside the door. Eppie opened it and welcomed Mr and Mrs Godfrey Cass in her polite, country way.

'I'm sorry that it's so late,' Nancy said. She looked pale and worried. Eppie put out two chairs and stood by Silas.

Godfrey was frightened, too, but he hid his fear. 'I'm pleased about the money, Marner,' he said. 'My family did you wrong. I'm very sorry and I want to repay you for your trouble. I have behaved badly too – it's not just my brother, Marner.'

Silas looked at him in surprise. 'Sir, you've helped us in many ways,' he said. 'The money wasn't your fault – and it's here now.'

'You can look at it in that way, Marner, but I can't,' Godfrey told him. 'You worked hard for that money.'

'Oh, sir,' Silas smiled. 'Work was my only friend in my time of trouble.'

Godfrey did not understand. He was thinking his own thoughts and went on: 'Yes, you worked hard and you need a rest. You're not a young man. We're all growing old and that money on the table isn't very much. It won't last for ever. Remember – there are two of you!'

'Even when I'm old, Eppie and I will be happy enough, sir,' Silas said quietly. 'We don't want much. Not many men like me save so much. Perhaps the money's nothing to someone like you, sir. But it's a lot to us .'

Godfrey was not pleased with himself. He was not explaining his business well. The difficulty of it surprised him.

'You should plan for your future,' he said quietly. 'You want Eppie to enjoy life, don't you? She's not as strong as the other village girls and a hard life and hard work will be bad for her. If a rich family takes her, she won't have to work hard. They can turn her into a lady and leave her their money.'

A sudden fear shook Silas. 'What do you mean, sir?' he asked.

'Mrs Cass and I have no children,' Godfrey explained slowly. 'We have a good home and more than enough money. But we are the only ones who enjoy them. We want to have somebody in place of a daughter. We want to have Eppie as our own child.

After all this time, you'll be pleased, won't you? Eppie, of course, will always love and remember you. She'll come and see you very often. We'll help you in every possible way.'

Eppie put her hand on Silas's shoulder. At first he could not speak, but after a moment he said, 'Eppie, my dear, I won't keep you, if you want to go.'

Eppie felt her father's deep unhappiness. She thanked the Casses politely and then she said, 'I can't leave my father. Nobody can be closer to me. Thank you again, but I can't be a lady. I can't leave my friends.'

Her voice shook a little. With a cry Silas put his hand on hers. Nancy's eyes were full of tears. She was sorry for Eppie and for Godfrey too, but she said nothing.

Eppie's words were a complete surprise to Godfrey. After all these years he was doing the right thing. Why couldn't Eppie and Silas understand that? When he spoke again, he sounded angry.

'I have the strongest of all reasons for my suggestion, Eppie,' he said slowly. He turned to Silas. 'Marner – Eppie is my child and I need to look after her. It's my duty and not the duty of any other man. She's my own child. Her mother was my wife.'

When Eppie cried out, it freed Silas from his fear. He knew that she did not want to leave him. The thought made him stronger and some of his old hate came back. 'Why didn't you tell me 16 years ago?' he said in a cold, hard voice. 'I didn't love her then. Why do you want to take her now? Why don't you take the heart out of my body? God gave her to me when you did not want her. I took her in, and in God's eyes she is my child. She isn't yours because you never accepted her.'

'I know. I was wrong. I'm very sorry,' Godfrey said quietly.

'Sixteen years don't change because you're sorry. You call yourself her father. Hearts don't change for that reason. She called me Father as soon as she could say the word. And she does to this day.'

'I can't leave my father. Nobody can be closer to me.'

'I've said I'm sorry.' Godfrey spoke more loudly. 'Listen to me, Marner. Think about it. She's not going out of your life. She'll be very near and she'll visit you very often. She'll feel the same towards you.'

'Oh, will she?' said Silas in an even angrier voice. 'How will she feel the same? Every day we eat the same food and drink the same drink. We have the same thoughts. She'll feel the same? That's empty talk.'

'You love Eppie, Marner,' Godfrey said angrily. 'Don't you want a happy life for her? Or is your own enjoyment more important to you? Remember your age, and hers. Time is short. Perhaps she'll marry some village boy. Then her chance of a good home and my money will end. You're taking that chance away from her. I don't want to hurt you – you did so much, and I did nothing – but I have to look after my own daughter. It's my duty.'

These words woke deep memories in Eppie. She turned her thoughts from her old, much-loved father towards this new strange father. When she was a baby, he was only a shadow. This shadow had put a wedding ring on her mother's finger. But here was the real man. Her thoughts went back to his life with her mother. They turned then to a possible life with him in the future. She did not want this life. She did not like him as a father. But she did not decide for this reason. She decided because she loved Silas.

Silas was frightened of losing her. But nothing mattered to Silas except that Eppie should be happy. After a long time he spoke, and his voice shook. 'I'll say no more. Have your own way. Speak to the child. I won't stop you.'

Godfrey looked at his daughter. She was not a child any more. He was afraid that she hated him.

'Eppie, my dear,' he said, 'Marner was a good father to you. We shall always want you to show him your love and thanks. We'll always give you our help in this. But we too ask for your love. I was not a good father. I know that. The rest of my life will be different. I want to please you in every way. As my only child you'll have everything. And my wife will be the best of mothers. After all these years you'll have a mother's love again.'

'My dear, you'll be everything to me,' said Nancy in her soft voice. 'Our life will be complete with our daughter.'

Eppie did not move. She kept her hand on Silas's shoulder, and spoke in a strong, cold voice. She thanked them both again for their offers.

'You are very kind, sir, and your suggestion is too much for me. I shall never be happy again if I leave my father alone here. I can't think of the idea. We are happy together every day of our lives. I can't enjoy anything without him. He had nobody before me – what will he have if I go now? From the first he looked after me and loved me. I'll stay with him for ever. Nobody will ever come between him and me.'

Nancy looked at Godfrey. But he was looking down at the floor. His thoughts were far away. She was his wife. She had to help him.

'My dear,' she said. 'I understand. Of course you want to stay here. But you have a duty to your real father. He is offering you his home. Will it be right if you refuse him?'

'In my heart I know only one father,' said Eppie. Her eyes were wet with tears. 'He'll sit in a corner of our little home and I shall do everything for him. I don't want any other home. I can't live like a lady. I like poor people and their houses and their ways. And I'm going to marry a poor man. I've promised. He'll live here, and together we shall look after Father.'

So Godfrey's plan failed. Eppie did not want his love. It was too late. This was the result of his worst actions. His face was red and his eyes hurt. Suddenly he felt a great need for air.

'We should go,' he said in a low voice. And without another word he left the room.

Nancy got up. 'We won't talk any more now. We want the best for you, my dear – and for you too, Marner. We shall come and see you again. It's late now.'

She said goodbye and left them.

Chapter 17   Husband and Wife

Godfrey did not speak on the way home. After their return, he sat down in his favourite chair. Nancy stood near him and waited. At last Godfrey turned his head towards her. They looked at each other. They did not need words.

After a time he put out his hand. Nancy took it, and he pulled her towards him.

'That's the end of that,' he said.

She kissed him. 'Yes,' she said, 'we can't continue with your plan, can we? She doesn't want to be our daughter, and we can't make her come here. We can't change her mind, either.'

'No,' Godfrey agreed. 'Some duties are different from others. If you borrow money, you can pay it back at any time. You pay a little more, that's all. But other duties won't wait. It's too late now. Marner was right. If a man refuses a good thing, another man will have it. I didn't want people to know about my child at that time. Now I do, but it has to stay a secret.'

'So you won't tell people about you and Eppie?' Nancy asked after a few moments.

'No. What good will it do? She has chosen her own life, and I'll help her in every possible way. She wants to marry someone, doesn't she? I need to know his name.'

'We won't trouble Father and Priscilla then,' said Nancy. 'We'll only tell them about Dunsey. We should do that, of course.'

'I'll put the facts in a letter, perhaps,' said Godfrey. 'People found out about Dunsey by chance – I don't want them to find out about me in the same way. At the end of my life they can open the letter and learn the truth. But I don't want to tell anyone now. Eppie can be happy in her own way. Oh, I remember now. Doesn't she want to marry Aaron Winthrop? I saw him with her and Marner at the church.'

'He's a good young man, and he works hard,' said Nancy. She wanted to make her husband feel better.

After a time Godfrey said in a sad voice: 'She's a very nice, pretty girl, isn't she, Nancy?'

'Yes, dear – and she has your hair and eyes. I didn't see that before, but it's very plain to me now.'

'She doesn't like me, though, does she? Not now she knows I'm her real father. She liked me once. But she changed when I told her the truth.'

'Marner is a father to her. She didn't like the idea of change.'

'No, she doesn't like me. The wrong to her is not the only reason. She thinks that her mother's death is my fault. And I will have to accept that. I can never tell her about that woman's life. It *is* my fault. I was crazy when I married her. I behaved badly towards you. And then I behaved badly towards the child.'

Nancy said nothing. He was right, and she did not want to help him with a lie. After a little he went on in a softer voice, 'But I've got *you*, Nancy. And I'm very lucky; nothing matters except that.'

'You are always good to me, Godfrey. Just accept what God decides. Then I shall be completely happy.'

'I'll try to accept the situation, my dear. It's not too late. But I can't change the past. It *is* too late for that.'

272

Chapter 18   New Beginnings

In Raveloe, weddings were usually in the spring. It was the best time, because all the plants were starting to flower. People were not too busy on the farms and the weather was not too cold.

The sun was very warm on Eppie's wedding day. This was lucky because her wedding dress was a very light one. Eppie could not pay for it herself. But she chose it and Mrs Godfrey Cass bought it for her. It was made of white cotton with a few small pink flowers on it.

Before the wedding she said to her father, 'I'm not leaving you, Father. There won't be any changes and you'll have Aaron as your son.'

After the wedding she walked from the church through the village. One hand was on her husband's arm and the other held her father's hand. Her white dress and golden hair shone in the sun. Dolly Winthrop was with them.

Miss Priscilla Lammeter, Nancy's sister, and her father drove past at that moment. They watched with enjoyment; everyone loves a wedding. They were visiting Nancy because Godfrey was away. He could not go to the wedding but he was paying for it. 'Of course he feels a great interest in the weaver,' Priscilla thought. 'His own brother stole from the poor man.'

'Why couldn't Nancy have a child like that?' she said to her father. 'Nothing can take the place of a child in a family.'

'Yes, my dear,' said her father. 'One feels that in later life. Old people are young again in the company of children.'

Nancy came out and welcomed her father and sister. The wedding group went on its way until they came to the quarry.

There were many changes to Silas's house and it had a garden now. Godfrey Cass was paying for everything. He even offered Silas and Eppie a new home, but they wanted to stay at the quarry.

One hand was on her husband's arm and the other held her
father's hand.

The garden was full of flowers. It had a stone wall around it and the gate at the front was open. Four very happy people walked through the gate and the flowers welcomed them.

'Oh, Father,' said Eppie, 'we have such a pretty home! Nobody in the world is happier than we are.'

ACTIVITIES

Chapters 1–3

Before you read

1 Read the first few sentences of Chapter 1. What have you learnt about Silas Marner? His life is going to change. In what way, do you think?

2 Find these words in your dictionary:

   behave coin fault God hunt loom

   Match the words with their meanings.

   1 *behave*   **a** to search for people or animals
   2 *coin*   **b** many people believe that this being made the world
   3 *fault*   **c** a machine for making cloth
   4 *God*   **d** to act well or badly
   5 *hunt*   **e** a piece of money made of metal
   6 *loom*   **f** a weakness in someone

3 Find these words in your dictionary. Use them to complete the sentences below.

   master quarry Squire truth weave

   a You can use a loom to .... cloth.
   b The old .... was deep and full of water.
   c He was a .... builder; he was very good at his job.
   d The .... owned a lot of land.
   e She lied; she did not tell the ....

After you read

Answer the questions.

4 Who:

   a steals money from the church in Lantern Yard?
   b marries Sarah?
   c moves from a big town to the village of Raveloe?
   d gets well with Silas's help?
   e hides money in leather bags under the floor?
   f wants to marry Nancy Lammeter?
   g is married to Molly?
   h is going to sell a horse?

277

5 Why:

  a does Silas not go to church in Raveloe?

  b are the villagers angry with Silas?

  c is Dunstan unpopular in the village?

  d do Godfrey and Dunstan Cass need money quickly?

6 Work in pairs or groups. Both Silas Marner and Godfrey Cass are very unhappy. Choose one of them. Discuss the reasons for his unhappiness. Suggest solutions to his problems.

Chapters 4–6

Before you read

7 How do you think the story will continue? Choose two of these possibilities.

  a Godfrey will tell the Squire about his marriage.

  b Dunstan will not return from the hunt.

  c Silas will lose all his money.

  d The villagers will show their dislike of Silas.

  e Silas will fall in love.

After you read

  8 Which answers to Activity 7 are correct?

  9 Give reasons for the truth of these statements:

  a Dunstan is a very silly young man.

  b Dunstan is a criminal.

10 Answer these questions:

  a Where exactly does Silas keep his money?

  b How does Dunstan find it so easily?

11 Work in pairs. Imagine that Silas returns to his house while Dunstan is taking the money from the hole.

  Student A: You are Silas. How do you feel? What do you say to Dunstan?

  Student B: You are Dunstan. How do you feel? What do you say to Silas?

  Act out the conversation.

278

Chapters 7–9

Before you read

12 Do you think that the villagers will find Dunstan? If so, how will they find him? If not, why not?

13 Find these words in your dictionary:

duty pedlar Rector

Are these sentences true?

a Your *duty* is something you must do.

b A *pedlar* works in a shop.

c A *Rector* is a government officer.

14 A *tinder-box* holds the things you need to start a fire. *Tinder* is a word used to describe something that burns easily. Name some things that burn easily.

After you read

15 Answer the questions about the titles of these chapters.

The Hunt for the Thief

a Who do the villagers think that the thief is?

b Do they find the thief?

c Why is Godfrey not interested in the hunt for the thief?

Father and Son

d Who are the father and son?

e Which one of his secrets does Godfrey tell his father? Which one does he not tell him?

f Does either of them feel better at the end of their conversation?

Good Neighbours

g Who are the 'good neighbours'?

h How do they try to help?

i How successful are they?

16 Describe what the villagers in Raveloe do and do not do on Sundays. Is Sunday (or another day of the week) different from other days for you or your family? In what way?

Chapters 10–12

Before you read

17 Imagine the conversation that Godfrey is going to have with Nancy at the New Year dance. What will they say to each other?

18 Find these words in your dictionary:

opium scissors

Which one:

a cuts paper?

b is a medicine?

c is metal and sharp?

d is a painkiller?

After you read

19 Who says these words? Who is he/she talking to?

a 'I want to be with you. That's more important than anything.'

b 'I will never take you to Raveloe . . . I will die first.'

c 'Nobody will take her away from me, except her family.'

d 'You see! She likes you best.'

e 'If she makes a bit of trouble, I'll live with it.'

20 How does Eppie succeed in leaving Silas's house alone?

21 Discuss the changes to these people's lives in these three chapters.

a Silas b Eppie c Godfrey

Chapters 13–15

Before you read

22 In this part of the book, the story continues 16 years later. What do you think the lives of Silas Marner and Godfrey Cass are like now?

23 Find the word *adopt* in your dictionary. If a person *adopts* a child, do they:

a take the child into their own family?

b say they do not want the child?

After you read

24 Fill the spaces with the names of people from the story.

Sixteen years later, ¹.............. and Eppie are living very happily together. ².............. and Eppie are thinking about marriage. They plan to live with ³.............. after the wedding. Godfrey is married to ⁴.............. . Their only sadness is that they have not got a child. Then ⁵..............'s body is found in the quarry with ⁶..............'s money. Godfrey tells his wife about his first marriage. She says that he should bring ⁷.............. to their home.

25 Suggest how Dunstan fell to the bottom of the quarry.

Chapters 16–18

Before you read

26 When Godfrey and his wife invite Eppie to their home, how will Eppie feel? What do you think she will decide to do?

After you read

27 Are these statements true or false?

a Silas is happy to have his money again.

b Eppie is pleased by Godfrey's invitation.

c Eppie already knew who her father was.

d Everyone will now know her father's name.

e Godfrey will never do anything for Eppie again.

f Eppie and Aaron continue to live with Silas.

28 Discuss what these people say.

a Nancy: '. . . you have a duty to your real father.' Do you think that Eppie has a duty to Godfrey?

b Godfrey: 'She thinks that her mother's death is my fault.' What do you think?

Writing

29 Godfrey says that he will write about his past in a letter. People will be able to read the letter after his death. Write the letter for him.

30 Write a letter from Eppie to Godfrey after the visit that Godfrey and Nancy made to Silas's home. Explain your (Eppie's) feelings in the letter.

31 'The good people in the story find happiness; those who behave badly are unhappy.' Is this true, do you think?

32 Imagine that you are Silas. Write about one day in your life soon after Eppie comes to live with you. What is new for you? How is your life changing?

33 Write the story of the book in 150–200 words.

34 Did you enjoy reading this book? Why/why not? Give your reasons.

Answers for the Activities in this book are published in our free resource packs for teachers, the Penguin Readers Factsheets, or available on a separate sheet. Please write to your local Pearson Education office or to: Marketing Department, Penguin Longman Publishing, 5 Bentinck Street, London W1M 5RN.